PRIMARY

MATHEMATICS

6A

Home Instructor's

Guide

Authored by: Jennifer Hoerst
Printed by: Sonlight Curriculum, Ltd.

For a free catalog of Sonlight Curriculum homeschool materials

Go to:
www.sonlight.com/catsurvey.html

Or e-mail:
catalog@sonlight.com

Or write:
Sonlight Curriculum, Ltd.
8042 South Grant Way
Littleton, CO 80122-2705
USA

Printed in the United States of America

Sonlight Curriculum, in an effort to help purchasers of the Singapore Primary Mathematics 6A Textbook and Workbook is providing this Home Instructor's Guide. As this is the first version produced, we would welcome your feedback and input. If you find errors, we would also welcome your pointing these out to us. To give us feedback or to note corrections, please send an email to purchasing@sonlight.com, or to the author at jenny@singmath.com, or you may send via the postal system to Sonlight Curriculum, Ltd., 8042 South Grant Way, Littleton, CO, 80122-2705.

As errors are detected and corrected, you may find the error corrections posted online at the author's web site, http://www.singmath.com. Additional help may be obtained at the forum linked there. **NOTE:** This site is the sole property of Jennifer Hoerst and is not a site maintained by Sonlight Curriculum. This site is offered solely as a courtesy to help purchasers see corrections as Jennifer Hoerst posts them. All corrections captured will be included in updates to the manuals prior to their reprinting.

Preface and General Instructions

This guide is meant to help instructors using *Primary Mathematics 6A* when teaching one student or a small group of students. It should be used as a guide and adapted as needed. It contains

 objectives,

 notes to the instructor, providing added explanation of concepts, and

 instructional ideas and suggested activities,

to reinforce concepts from the

 corresponding textbook pages, learning tasks, and

 "homework" assignments.

It also has

 answers and solutions to all the learning tasks, workbook exercises and reviews, and textbook practices and reviews.

The learning tasks in the text should be discussed with the student and additional explanation provided when necessary.

Practices and reviews in the text can, for the most part, be done independently by the student. Since some of the practice questions are challenging, they provide good opportunities for discussion or as additional learning tasks. Reviews cover material from all previous levels of *Primary Mathematics*. If your student has problems with some of the reviews and you have not used earlier levels, you should consider getting the textbooks for *Primary Mathematics* 4A through 5B and having your student do the pertinent units from those books.

Included is a suggested weekly schedule.

This guide can be used with both the third edition and the U.S. edition of *Primary Mathematics 6A*. U.S. spellings and conventions are used in this guide, but answers are given for both editions, except for the number words. In writing out numbers, the U.S. edition does not use the word "and" for whole numbers (e.g. four hundred one thousand, sixty-two). The 3d edition uses "and" in the number words for whole numbers (e.g. four hundred and one thousand and sixty-two).

3d› indicates portions pertaining only to the third edition, and

US› indicates portions pertaining only to the US edition (except for number words).

I wish to thank Lisa Boydstun, Jo Oehrlein, and Kendra Hoerst for their invaluable help in proofing parts of this guide.

Contents

Weekly Schedule

WB: Workbook
TB: Textbook

	Unit	Part	Lesson	Text pages	Exercises	Materials
1	1 Algebra	1 Algebraic Expressions	(1) Simple Algebraic Expressions	6-9	WB Ex. 1	
			(2) Algebraic Expressions	10-11	WB Ex. 2	
			(3) Simplifying Algebraic Expressions	12-13	WE Ex. 3	Markers Unit cubes
			Practice	14	TB Practice 1A	
2	2 Solid Figures	1 Drawing Solid Figures	(1) Drawing Solid Figures	15-16	WB Ex. 4	
		2 Nets	(1) Nets	17-18	WB Ex. 5	Square graph paper
			(2) Nets from Solids	19	WB Ex. 6	
			(3) Solids from Nets	20	WB Ex. 7	
3	3 Ratio	1 Ratio and Fraction	(1) Ratios	21-23	WB Ex. 8	Counters
			(2) Ratios and Fractions	24-26	WB Ex. 9	
			(3) Word Problems I	27	WB Ex. 10	Blocks or counters
			(4) Word Problems II	28	WB Ex. 11	
4			Practice	29	TB Practice 3A	Wiggle Woods CD-ROM Primary 6: Ratio: Learn and Explore, Activity
		2 Ratio and Proportion	(1) Ratio and Proportion	30-32	WB Ex. 12	
			Practice	33	TB Practice 3B	Wiggle Woods CD-ROM Primary 6: Ratio: Challenge
5		3 Changing Ratios	(1) Finding the New Ratio	34-36	WB Ex. 13	
			(2) Finding Amounts Using Changing Ratios	36-37	WB Ex. 14	
			Practice	38	TB Practice 3C	
6	Review				TB Review A TB Review B	
7					WB Review 1	
8	4 Percentage	1 Part of a Whole as a Percentage	(1) Fraction as Percentage	47-50	WB Ex. 15	
			(2) Percentage, Fractions, and Decimals	50	WB Ex. 16	
			(3) Word Problems	51	WB Ex. 17	
			(4) Percentage of a Percentage	51	WB Ex. 18	

Additional Materials

Markers from a game, counters, small cubes or other small items.

Square graph paper
There are some in the appendix that can be copied.

Wiggle Woods CD-ROM
Optional computer CD-ROM with activities and games.

Unit 1 – Algebra

Part 1 – Algebraic Expressions

(1) Simple Algebraic Expressions (pp. 6-9)

> ➤ Use letters to represent unknown numbers.
> ➤ Write simple algebraic expressions in one variable.
> ➤ Find the value of a simple algebraic expression using substitution.

An algebraic expression is an arithmetic expression involving an unknown number. The unknown number is represented by a letter called a *variable*. For example, in the expression $n + 2$, n is the variable. A variable can take any *value*. If we assign a value of 3 to n, then the expression can be evaluated as $3 + 2 = 5$. If we assign a value of 5 to n, the expression can be evaluated as $5 + 2 = 7$.

In the secondary levels, students will learn about algebraic equations, where the answer to the expression is given, in which case the variable is fixed and can take on only one value. For example, in $n + 2 = 7$, the only value n can have is 5.

Although you can use the term *variable* for the unknown number in discussions, do not dwell on this term. As students proceed in pre-algebra and algebra, letters can also stand for constants or parameters or to name objects. For this section, your student should think of the letter as standing for a number in an arithmetic expression. The expression can be evaluated by assigning a specific value to the letter. The letter then becomes a number.

In earlier levels of Primary Mathematics, student learned to draw part-whole and comparison models using bars to represent both known and unknown quantities. They could think of a variable as a bar that can stretch or shrink.

$$\overset{\displaystyle n}{\longleftrightarrow}\ \overset{\displaystyle 2}{\longleftrightarrow}$$

In ⬚⬚⬚⬚⬚⬚⬚▬ the length of the bar labeled n, and the total length

$$\underset{\displaystyle n+2}{\longleftrightarrow}$$

of both bars, can be longer or shorter in comparison for the bar for 2, depending on the value of n (hence the dotted outline for the bar for n).

$$\overset{\displaystyle n}{\longleftrightarrow}\qquad\qquad \overset{\displaystyle 2}{\longleftrightarrow}$$

In ⬚⬚⬚⬚⬚⬚▬ all 3 unit bars would be longer or shorter by

$$\underset{\displaystyle (3 \times n) + 2}{\longleftrightarrow}$$

the same amount depending on the value of n.

If the letter is replacing a whole number, the expression can also be visualized as a bag or box holding an unknown number of unit cubes or items.   Each identical bag holds the same number.

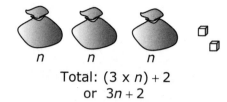

Total: $(3 \times n) + 2$
or $3n + 2$

In this section, students will build expressions for a particular situation and then evaluate them.   They will first build expressions using addition or subtraction, and then using multiplication or division.   Note that the multiplication sign can be removed when expressing a multiple of a variable; $3 \times n = 3n$. The number is written first, then the variable. So $n3$ means $n \times 3$, but it should be written as the equivalent expression $3n$.

Students will then substitute a value for the variable.   For example, they will be asked to evaluate $3n$ for $n = 2$. Substitute 2 for n, thus $3n = 3 \times 2 = 6$.

Algebraic expressions involving division are normally written as a fraction.   So $m \div 3$ is usually represented as $\frac{m}{3}$. If necessary, during the discussion remind your student that $12 \div 3$ is the same as $\frac{12}{3}$. If m is used instead of 12, we can write $m \div 3$ as $\frac{m}{3}$.

 Page 6
   Discuss this page with your student.   After determining that Limei is 2 years older than Angela, add an equation to the second column of the table:

Ask your student if he sees a pattern in the equations.   In each, 2 is added to Angela's age. Tell your student that if we don't know Angela'a age at first, or if we want a general expression to show how Limei's age relates to Angela's age, we can use the letter n to stand for Angela's age. The letter n can be any whole number that makes sense within the context of this situation and represents Angela's age.

Angela's age	Limei's age
6	$6 + 2 = 8$
7	$7 + 2 = 9$
8	$8 + 2 = 10$
9	$9 + 2 = 11$
10	$10 + 2 = 12$
n	$n + 2$

Limei's age could then be written as $n + 2$. Add another line to the table to show this. Point out that we are *expressing* Limei's age *in terms of* Angela's age.   If we say that n stands for Angela's age, then we can say that we are expressing Limei's age in terms of n.   If we are told what Angela's age is, we can *substitute* the number we are given for Angela's age in for n, and then find Limei's age.

You can also show this with a bar diagram.

Learning Tasks 1-9, pp. 7-9
If necessary, use a diagram to help build the expressions. Some examples are given here in the answers.

 1.   (a) **13 years**   (b) **$(x+8)$ years**

2.   (a) **\$8**   (b) **\$$(m-2)$**

3.   (b) **3 kg**

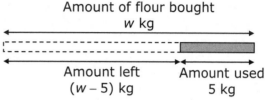

Amount of flour bought
w kg

Amount left
$(w-5)$ kg

Amount used
5 kg

4.   (b) $4n = 4 \times 8 =$ **32** (c) $4n = 4 \times 11 =$ **44**

5.   (b) **21**   Total marbles
x

7.   (a) **12**   (b)

$\dfrac{x}{8}$

8.   (a) **\$4**

9.   (a) $n+4 = 6+4$ (b) $10+n = 10+6$ (c) $15-n = 15-6$
                 $= \textbf{10}$ $= \textbf{16}$ $= \textbf{9}$

     (d) $n-6 = 6-6$ (e) $4n = 4 \times 6$ (f) $10n = 10 \times 6$
                  $= \textbf{0}$ $= \textbf{24}$ $= \textbf{60}$

     (g) $\dfrac{n}{2} = \dfrac{6}{2} = \textbf{3}$ (h) $\dfrac{n}{6} = \dfrac{6}{6} = \textbf{1}$ (i) $\dfrac{n}{12} = \dfrac{6}{12} = \dfrac{\textbf{1}}{\textbf{2}}$

 Workbook Exercise 1

(2) Algebraic Expressions (pp. 10-11)

➢ Write algebraic expressions in one variable involving more than one operation.
➢ Solve algebraic expressions with substitution.

 Make up a simple story problem involving multiplication or division where you use boxes for numbers. Have your student substitute in appropriate numbers and write an equation. Limit the discussion to whole numbers. Then have her replace one of the numbers with a letter and write the equation. Draw diagrams to illustrate the situation. Then elaborate on the situation to generate expressions that involve addition or subtraction as well. For example:

Ann's allowance is \$☐ every week. How much will she get in ☐ weeks?

Fill in the box with suitable numbers, such as \$10 and 4. In 4 weeks Ann will get \$10 × \$4 = \$40. Substitute \$m for \$10. In 4 weeks she will get \$4m.

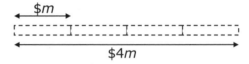

Or substitute w for weeks. In w weeks she will get \$10w.

During those 4 weeks, Ann also earned \$☐ from babysitting. How much total money did she make in those 4 weeks if she earned \$12 from babysitting and made \$m a week?

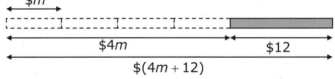

Ask your student how much money Ann made if she got an allowance of \$12 a week. What would she have made if her allowance was \$20 a week?

During ☐ weeks, Paula made ☐, ☐ of it was from babysitting and the rest from a weekly allowance. How much Paula's weekly allowance? Substitute numbers such as 8 for weeks, \$100 for the total amount, and \$20 for babysitting. The equation would be $\frac{\$100 - \$20}{4}$. Substitute a letter for one of the boxes, for example b for the amount made babysitting. The equation would be $\frac{\$100 - b}{4}$. Ask how much her allowance would have been if she made \$10 from babysitting.

➤ Tell your student you have a cube that measures ☐ on the side. Substitute in a number for the box and find an equation for the volume of the cube. If the cube is 4 cm on the side, the volume is $4 \times 4 \times 4 = 64$ cm³. What if the cube were s cm on the side? The volume is $s \times s \times s$ cm³. Tell your student that rather than writing this as sss cm³, we write it as s³ cm³. The 3 in this expression is called an *exponent*. An *exponent* of 3 means the number multiplied by itself 3 times. Ask your student to write out some expressions where the variable has an exponent using multiplication. For example:

$$m^4 = m \times m \times m \times m$$
$$m^4 - 2 = m \times m \times m \times m - 2$$

 Learning Tasks 10-17, pp. 10-11

 11. **7**   12. (b) **19**   13. **4**

14. (a) **7**   (b) **10**

15. (a) **9**   (b) **18**   (c) $\dfrac{9}{5}$

16. (a) **8**   (b) **9**   (c) **12**

17. (a) $\dfrac{4a}{3} = \dfrac{4 \times 5}{3}$
$= \dfrac{20}{3}$
$= \mathbf{6\dfrac{2}{3}}$

(b) $8 + 3a = 8 + (3 \times 5)$
$= 8 + 15$
$= \mathbf{23}$

(c) $2a - 3 = (2 \times 5) - 3$
$= 10 - 3$
$= \mathbf{7}$

(d) $\dfrac{a}{3} + 2 = \dfrac{5}{3} + 2$
$= 1\dfrac{2}{3} + 2$
$= \mathbf{3\dfrac{2}{3}}$

(e) $\dfrac{3a - 4}{2} = \dfrac{(3 \times 5) - 4}{2}$
$= \dfrac{11}{2}$
$= \mathbf{5\dfrac{1}{2}}$

(f) $\dfrac{2a + 5}{5} = \dfrac{(2 \times 5) + 5}{5}$
$= \dfrac{15}{5}$
$= \mathbf{3}$

(g) $2a^2 - 3$
$= (2 \times 5 \times 5) - 3$
$= 50 - 3$
$= \mathbf{47}$

(h) $a^3 + 5 = (5 \times 5 \times 5) + 5$
$= 125 + 5$
$= \mathbf{130}$

(i) $a^3 - 5 = (5 \times 5 \times 5) - 5$
$= 125 - 5$
$= \mathbf{120}$

 Workbook Exercise 2

(3) Simplifying Algebraic Expressions (pp. 12-13)

 ➢ Simplify algebraic expressions in one variable involving addition and subtraction of algebraic terms.

 In algebraic expressions, algebraic terms are separated by $+$ or $-$ signs.   The expression $2y + 3$ has two terms, and $3y + 4y - 3$ has 3 terms. A coefficient is the number part of the term including a variable. In $3y$, 3 is a coefficient. A term that contains only numbers is called a constant. In $2y + 3$, 3 is a constant.

Like terms are those terms in an expression that have the exact same variables *and* exponents. $2y$ and $3y$ are like terms, $2a$ and $2b$ or $2y$ and $3y^2$ are not.

Algebraic expressions can be simplified by combining like terms and constants. We can do this by first grouping like terms. The $+$ or $-$ sign must go with the term. For example:

$$4y - 5 - 2y + 10 = 4y - 2y + 10 - 5 = 2y + 5$$

The fact that the -5 term can be moved after the $+10$ term can cause confusion for some students. In *Primary Mathematics 5A*, students learned to add or subtract from left to right. This automatically keeps the minus with the term that follows it, so that it is being subtracted. Addition and subtraction can be done in any order, as long as the term is being added or subtracted according to the operation sign in front of it. Thus

$$3 - 10 + 8 = 3 + 8 - 10 = 1.$$

Similarly

$$3y - 10y + 8y = 3y + 8y - 10y = y$$

Until students learn about negative numbers, there will be occasions when they need to rearrange the terms in an expression in order to avoid negative numbers. They can do so, as long as they realize the operation just before it is to be treated as part of the term and moved with it.

In this unit, students will only encounter expressions with like terms in one variable and constants.   The expressions will not include fraction or decimal coefficients here.

For some students, a concrete representation may be helpful. Choose two types of uniform objects, one which could represent a bag with the same number in it, i.e. the variable, and the other ones. For example, a playing piece or a marker from a game could represent the variable. It can stand for any number. Unit cubes from a base-10 set can represent the constant values. Set out markers and cubes for terms to be added, then take away some for terms to be subtracted.

So for $4y - 5 - 2y + 10$ you can set out 4 markers for $4y$ and 10 cubes for 10, then take away two of the markers and 5 cubes. Note that you start out with no markers or cubes. The first term and the ones with $+$ in front indicate what are added in, and the terms with $-$ in from indicate what are taken out.

You can also draw bags and marbles as in the text to illustrate the problems. Each bag is one variable and the marbles each stand for a one. Make sure your student understands that the bags within a problem all hold the same number of marbles, but can hold a different number than a previous problem, even if the variable has the same letter. You can first draw any bags or marbles that need to be added in, then cross out those that need to be subtracted out.

Learning Tasks 18-21, pp. 12-13
Discuss these problems with your student. Illustrate with objects or drawings as necessary. Rearrange terms if necessary by grouping like terms and constants, but if your student is not having difficulties do not require him to rewrite the problem with rearranged terms.

18. (b) **x**

19. (b) **6r**   (c) **3r + 3**   (d) **6r + 3**

21. (a) $5a + 4a =$ **9a**   (b) $8c - 5c =$ **3c**   (c) $7k - 2k + k =$ **6k**

(d) $3x + 6 - x$
$= 3x - x + 6$
$=$ **2x + 6**

(e) $7m + 7 - 2m$
$= 7m - 2m + 7$
$=$ **5m + 7**

(f) $5s + 10 + 2s$
$= 5s + 2s + 10$
$=$ **7s + 10**

(g) $2y + 5 + 3y - 2$
$= 2y + 3y + 5 - 2$
$=$ **5y + 3**

(h) $9 + 4m - 3m - 8$
$= 4m - 3m + 9 - 8$
$=$ **m + 1**

(i) $8r + 6 - 2r - 6$
$= 8r - 2r + 6 - 6$
$=$ **6r**

(j) $8p - 3p - p + 2$
$=$ **4p + 2**

(k) $8 + 8w + 5 - 2w$
$= 8w - 2w + 8 + 5$
$=$ **6w + 13**

(l) $7h + h - 4h - h$
$=$ **3h**

Workbook Exercise 3

Practice (p. 14)

   ➢ Practice forming, evaluating, and simplifying algebraic equations.

➤ Have your student come up with original story problems to go with some algebraic expressions. You can use some of the ones in Practice 1A.

➤ Have your student build algebraic equations for number tricks to show how they work. Ask your student to do the following number trick. You can illustrate with markers and cubes or drawings of bags and marbles.

- Choose a Number.
- Add 5.
- Double the result.
- Subtract 4.
- Divide the result by 2.
- Subtract the number you started with.
- The result is 3

Have him pick 4 different starting numbers and see that the result will always be 3. Guide him through writing algebraic expressions for each step, using a variable for the number picked:

Pick a number	n
Add 5	$n + 5$
Double the result	$2n + 10$ (note that both terms must be doubled)
Subtract 4	$2n + 10 - 4 = 2n + 6$
Divide the result by 2	$n + 3$
Subtract the number you started with	$n + 3 - n = 3$
	The result is always 3.

Have your student try another number trick with several numbers, determine what the result will always be, then prove that the result will always be that number using algebraic expressions:

- Pick a number below 1000
- Add 3
- Double the result
- Subtract 4 from the result
- Divide the result by 2
- Subtract the original number

Let your student come up with his own number trick.

Enrichment: This number trick involves two variables and the place value concept:

Pick a number between 0 and 9	n
Double it	$2n$
Add 5	$2n + 5$
Multiply by 5	$10n + 25$
Pick another number between 1 and 9 and add its value to the total	$10n + 25 + m$
Subtract 25 from the total	$10n + 25 + m - 25 = 10n + m$
The two digits of the result are the same as the two numbers.	$10n + m$ gives a 2 digit number with the first digit the ten and the second digit the m

Practice 1A (p. 14)

 1.
(a) $21 - y = 21 - 4$
   $\quad\ \ = \mathbf{17}$

(b) $y + 25 = 4 + 25$
   $\quad\quad\ = \mathbf{29}$

(c) $3y + 2 = 3 \times 4 + 2$
   $\quad\quad\ = 12 + 2$
   $\quad\quad\ = \mathbf{14}$

(d) $3y = 3 \times 4$
   $\quad\ \ = \mathbf{12}$

(e) $\dfrac{y}{2} = \dfrac{4}{2}$
   $\quad\ = \mathbf{2}$

(f) $\dfrac{y}{16} = \dfrac{4}{16}$
   $\quad\ = \dfrac{\mathbf{1}}{\mathbf{4}}$

(g) $\dfrac{2y - 5}{4} = \dfrac{2 \times 4 - 5}{4}$
   $\quad\quad\ = \dfrac{\mathbf{3}}{\mathbf{4}}$

(h) $y^2 + 4 = 4^2 + 4$
   $\quad\quad\ = 16 + 4$
   $\quad\quad\ = \mathbf{20}$

(i) $2y^2 = 2 \times 4 \times 4$
   $\quad\ \ = \mathbf{32}$

(j) $y^3 - 20$
   $\quad = 4 \times 4 \times 4 - 20$
   $\quad = 64 - 20$
   $\quad = \mathbf{44}$

(k) $\dfrac{3y}{2} = \dfrac{3 \times 4}{2}$
   $\quad\ \ = \dfrac{12}{2}$
   $\quad\ \ = \mathbf{6}$

(l) $50 - 3y^2$
   $\quad = 50 - 3 \times 4 \times 4$
   $\quad = 50 - 48$
   $\quad = \mathbf{2}$

2.
(a) $x + x + x = \mathbf{3x}$

(b) $3x + 4x = \mathbf{7x}$

(c) $6p - 4p = \mathbf{2p}$

3.
(a) $2p + 2p - p = \mathbf{3p}$

(b) $4r - 2r + 3r = \mathbf{5r}$

(c) $5f - f - 3f = \mathbf{f}$

4.
(a) $3c - 3c + c = \mathbf{c}$

(b) $5k + 7 - k$
   $\quad = 5k - k + 7$
   $\quad = \mathbf{4k + 7}$

(c) $6n + 3 + n + 2$
   $\quad = 6n + n + 3 + 2$
   $\quad = \mathbf{7n + 5}$

5.
(a) $7g - 2g + 2$
   $\quad = \mathbf{5g + 2}$

(b) $10x + 5 - 4x - 2$
   $\quad = 10x - 4x + 5 - 2$
   $\quad = \mathbf{6x + 3}$

(c) $3h + 8 - 3h + 2$
   $\quad = 3h - 3h + 8 + 2$
   $\quad = \mathbf{10}$

6.
(a) $\mathbf{\$(y + 1)}$

(b) $\$(8 + 1) = \mathbf{\$9}$

7.
(a) $\mathbf{3x\ m}$

(b) $3 \times 9 = \mathbf{27\ m}$

8.
(a) Peter's age = $\mathbf{3x + 4\ years}$

(b) $3 \times 4 + 4 = 12 + 4$
   $\quad\quad\quad\quad\ = \mathbf{16\ years}$

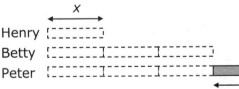

9.
(a) number of packets
   $= \dfrac{\mathbf{50 - y}}{\mathbf{2}}$

(b) $\dfrac{50 - 38}{2} = \dfrac{12}{2} = \mathbf{6}$

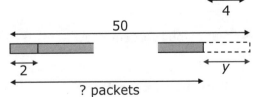

Unit 2 – Solid Figures

Part 1 – Drawing Solid Figures

(1) Drawing Solid Figures (pp. 15-16)

- ➤ Associate two-dimensional drawings with three-dimensional models or solids.
- ➤ Visualize pyramids, prisms, and cylinders from two-dimensional drawings.
- ➤ Determine the number and shapes of the faces of a two dimensional drawing of a solid.

 In *Primary Mathematics 4*, students learned to relate two-dimensional drawings of cubes and cuboids (rectangular prisms) to solids and to draw them using dot-paper. Here, your student will learn the two-dimensional representations of prisms, pyramids, and cylinders.

rectangular   triangular
prism   prism
(cuboid)

 If you have some 3-dimensional models of prisms, pyramids and cylinders, such as blocks, let your student examine them. Have him note that the prisms have two faces at either end that are the same, whereas pyramids do not. A rectangular pyramid has one rectangular base and four triangular faces meeting at a vertex opposite from the rectangular face. A triangular pyramid (tetrahedron) has a triangular base. Have your student count and name the different faces.

rectangular   triangular
pyramid   pyramid

cylinder

 Page 15
Learning Tasks 1-3, p. 16
Discuss p. 15. Note the differences between the two prisms and the pyramid, and that dotted lines are used to show hidden edges.

1. **C**

2. **A** 5 faces, 2 triangles   **B** 4 faces, 4 triangles   **C** 5 faces, 4 triangles

3. **D** (D is a pyramid, the others are prisms.)

 Have your student draw some 2-D representation of 3-D models.

 Workbook Exercise 4

Part 2 – Nets

(2) Nets (pp. 17-18)

  ➢ Form solids from nets.
  ➢ Identify nets of prisms and pyramids.

 A net of a solid is a figure which can be folded to form the surface of a solid. A solid can have more than one net.

Being able to visualize the net of a solid will help a student find the surface area of solids in later levels.

➤ If you have some cardboard boxes, have your student cut along various edges to flatten the boxes out, and then see how it folds up again into the box.

 Page 17
Learning Task 1, p. 18
Have your student trace and cut out the figures and then fold them to form the solid figure. For learning task 1, have him also draw a 2-dimensional representation of the solid formed.

1.   (a)   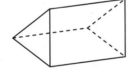   (b)

➤ Have your student draw the net of a cube. Give her a cube to examine first. There are 6 sides. Have her use some square graph paper to draw a net that will make a cube. The easiest way is to think of a cube as four sides, a top and a bottom. Four of the squares can be in a line. Then put the top square on one side of this line, and the bottom on the other. Have her cut it out and form the cube.

Have her experiment to see if she can find all possible nets that form a cube. There are 11 possibilities, apart from rotations and reflections. See if she can come up with some general rules for determining if a net of 6 squares can form a cube.

For nets of squares, the longest panel cannot have more than 4 squares. If the longest panel has 4 squares, the remaining 2 have to be placed on opposite sides. If the longest panel has 3 squares, the remaining 3 can be placed on either side but there must always be at least 2 free edges on either side of the longest panel. If the longest panel has 2 squares, the remaining 4 must be evenly distributed on either side such that there will be one free edge on either side of the panel. The 11 possible nets of a square are given here:

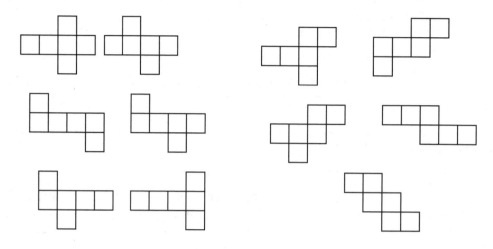

If your student is interested, have him determine the possible nets for a triangular pyramid or tetrahedron. There are two possibilities.

Sometimes liquids such as fruit juice come in a tetrahedron shaped package. They are made from a cylinder, which your student can try making. Make a cylinder of paper and tape the edge down. Pinch one end, and tape that. Now pinch the other end in the opposite direction, and tape that. It will naturally form a tetrahedron (with bulging sides).

 Workbook Exercise 5

(2) Nets from Solids (p. 19)

 ➤ Identify the net of a solid.

 In this section your student will see a 2-dimensional drawing of a solid and some nets, and will have to choose which of the nets could be a net of the solid.

Some students have good spatial visualization and can easily identify the net of a solid. Others have more difficulty. If your student has difficulty, have him trace the nets in this learning task and in workbook exercise 6 and physically try folding each of them into the solid and seeing concretely why they may or may not form the solid. If you have a scanner or copier, copy and enlarge the figures before tracing and cutting them out.

Even without tracing and cutting out the shapes, some choices can be easy to rule out. The nets need to have the same number and type of shapes as the faces of the solid. Any point on the net where three or four lines come together is going to be the vertex of the solid. So adjacent edges of the nets must be the same length as they will go together to form an edge.

 Learning Task 2, p. 19

 A and **D** are nets of the solid.

Have your student explain B and C cannot be nets of this solid. B does not have the right number of triangles. The bottom two edges of C are obviously of different lengths, so they won't be able to join along their lengths to form an edge.

 Workbook Exercise 6

(3) Solids from Nets (p. 20)

 ➢ Identify the solid formed from a net.

 In this section your student will see a net and several 2-dimensional drawings of solids, and will have to choose which of the solids could be formed from the net.

The solid must have the same number of faces with the same shapes as the net.

If your student has difficulty, copy the net and have her fold it into the solid.

 Learning Task 3, p. 20

 B is the solid formed from the net.

Have your student explain why the others can't be formed from the net. The net has 6 faces, whereas A has 6 and C has 4. D has 4 triangles and 1 rectangle, whereas the net has 3 rectangles and 2 triangles.

 Workbook Exercise 7

Unit 3 – Ratio

Part 1 – Ratio and Fraction

(1) Ratios (pp. 21-23)

> ➢ Compare quantities using ratios.
> ➢ Express a ratio in simplest form.

In *Primary Mathematics 5A*, students learned to write ratios which involved 2 or three quantities and to find the simplest form of a ratio. This is reviewed in this section.

A ratio is a comparison of the relative size of two or more quantities. Quantities can be compared without specifying the unit, as long as the unit is the same for both quantities. In measurement, a unit is required. A rope is 6 *feet* or 3 *meters* long. But one rope can be compared to another rope without specifying the unit, e.g. one rope is twice as long as the other. In a ratio, the unit can be anything we want it to be. The ratio between two ropes might be 2 : 1, whether we measured the rope in feet or meters, as long as we measured both ropes using the same unit of measurement. 2 : 1 means that there are 2 units to 1 unit.

The unit can also be a certain whole number. For example, the unit could be 100 fruit. Then if there are 200 apples and 300 oranges, the ratio of apples to oranges is 2 : 3.

Equivalent ratios are ratios where the relative sizes of the quantities remain the same, but the measurement unit is different for the equivalent ratio.

200 : 300, 20 : 30, 10 : 15, and 3 : 5 are equivalent ratios. Equivalent ratios can be found by multiplying or dividing each term by the same number. We can simplify a ratio by dividing each term by a common factor. If there is no common factor, the ratio is in its simplest form. 3 : 5 is a ratio in its simplest form.

➤ If necessary, you can review ratios with your student using counters. Set out 6 counters of one color (such as blue) and 12 of another (such as red). Tell your student that the ratio of red to blue counters is 6 : 12. Point out that the ratio of blue to red counters, 12 : 6, is different. Have your student group the counters by 2, 3, and 6 to show that the unit can be 1 counter, 2 counters, 3 counters, or 6 counters. You can draw unit bars under the counters to show how unit bars relate to ratios.

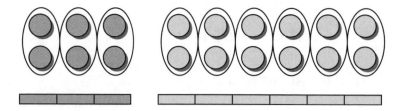

Ratio of blue counters to red counters = 3 : 6

    1 unit = 2 counters

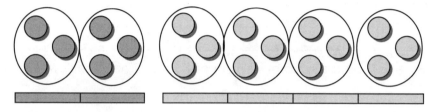

Ratio of blue counters to red counters = 2 : 4

    1 unit = 3 counters

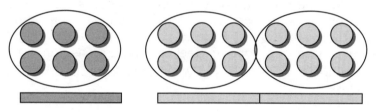

Ratio of blue counters to red counters = 1 : 2

    1 unit = 6 counters

Show how the different equivalent ratios can be derived from the first by dividing both terms by the same number.

    6 : 12 = 3 : 5 = 2 : 4 = 1 : 2

Ask your student to simplify 60 : 40 : 200. Point out that simplification can be done in several steps, dividing each term by an easily determined common factor (such as 2 until one number is no longer even, then 3 or 5) or in one step using the greatest common factor.

    60 : 40 : 200 = 30 : 20 : 100 (common factor 2)
               = 15 : 10 : 50 (common factor 2)
               = 3 : 2 : 10 (common factor 5)
    60 : 40 : 200 = 3 : 2 : 10 (common factor 20)

Page 21
Learning Tasks 1-5, pp. 22-23

 2 : 3

1. (b) **5 : 3**   (d) **4 : 3 : 5**

2. (b) **2 : 3 : 4**

3. (a) **7 : 9** (factor 5)   (b) **7 : 9 : 16** (factor 5)

4. **1 : 3 : 2** (factor 40)

5. **3 : 2 : 10** (factor 20)

 Workbook Exercise 8

---

(2) Ratios and Fractions (pp. 24-26)

  ➢ Express a ratio as a fraction of a quantity.
  ➢ Express a fraction of a quantity as a ratio.
  ➢ Determine how many times one quantity is as large as another given their ratios.
  ➢ Determine ratios from how many times one quantity is as large as another.

 Fractions are also used to compare quantities. One quantity can be $\frac{2}{3}$ as large as another. A ratio can be converted into a fraction, but it is important to determine what quantity is taken as the *whole*.

For example, the ratio of the length of A to B is 2 : 3. If B is taken as the whole, we can say that the length of A is $\frac{2}{3}$ *of* the length of B. Note that the quantity after the "of" is the quantity that is considered the whole. The length of A is a fraction *of* the length of *B*.   Note that the total is the bottom denominator of the fraction.

If we take the length of A as the whole instead, then we can express the length of B as a fraction *of* the length of A. We can also take the sum of A and B as the whole, or total, and express each length as a fraction of the total length.

A ☐☐
B ☐☐☐

A is $\frac{2}{3}$ of B

B is $\frac{3}{2}$ of A

A is $\frac{2}{5}$ of A and B

B is $\frac{3}{5}$ of A and B

In the problems in this section, the whole won't always be given last in the sentence. For example, the student may be asked to express the length of A as a fraction *of the length of B*, or to find what fraction *of the length of B* is the length of A.   In both cases, the whole or total is the length of B, and the answer is the same.

If we are given the fraction of one quantity to the other, we can convert it to a ratio.   If the length of A is $\frac{2}{3}$ of the length of B, we can diagram this relationship and easily see that the ratio of the length of A to the length of B is 2 : 3.

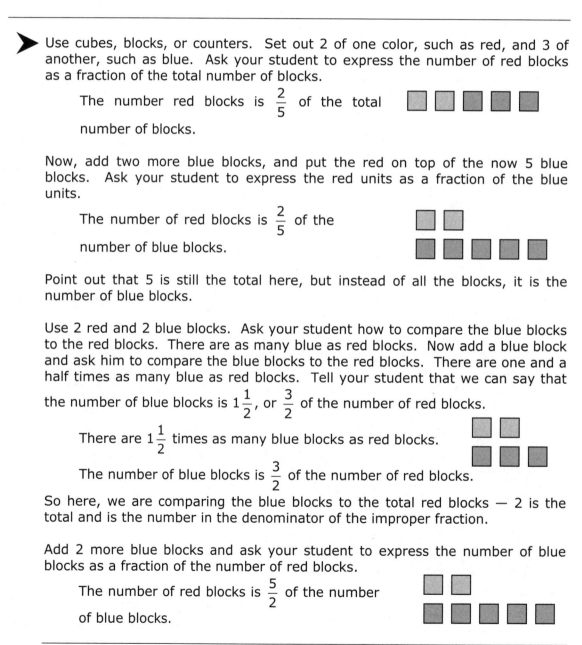

➤ Use cubes, blocks, or counters.   Set out 2 of one color, such as red, and 3 of another, such as blue.   Ask your student to express the number of red blocks as a fraction of the total number of blocks.

The number red blocks is $\frac{2}{5}$ of the total

number of blocks.

Now, add two more blue blocks, and put the red on top of the now 5 blue blocks.   Ask your student to express the red units as a fraction of the blue units.

The number of red blocks is $\frac{2}{5}$ of the

number of blue blocks.

Point out that 5 is still the total here, but instead of all the blocks, it is the number of blue blocks.

Use 2 red and 2 blue blocks.   Ask your student how to compare the blue blocks to the red blocks.   There are as many blue as red blocks.   Now add a blue block and ask him to compare the blue blocks to the red blocks.   There are one and a half times as many blue as red blocks.   Tell your student that we can say that the number of blue blocks is $1\frac{1}{2}$, or $\frac{3}{2}$ of the number of red blocks.

There are $1\frac{1}{2}$ times as many blue blocks as red blocks.

The number of blue blocks is $\frac{3}{2}$ of the number of red blocks.

So here, we are comparing the blue blocks to the total red blocks — 2 is the total and is the number in the denominator of the improper fraction.

Add 2 more blue blocks and ask your student to express the number of blue blocks as a fraction of the number of red blocks.

The number of red blocks is $\frac{5}{2}$ of the number

of blue blocks.

Learning Tasks 6-12, pp. 24-26
In discussing these tasks, emphasize the quantity that is to be taken as the whole, or the total, when expressing one quantity as a fraction of the other.

 6. (d) $\dfrac{5}{7}$ (f) $\dfrac{5}{2}$

7. (a) $\dfrac{\text{number of boys}}{\text{number of girls}} = \dfrac{4}{5}$ (b) $\dfrac{\text{number of girls}}{\text{number of boys}} = \dfrac{5}{4}$

8. $\dfrac{\text{Samy's money}}{\text{Jim's money}} = \dfrac{5}{3}$

9. (b) $\dfrac{350}{420} = \dfrac{5}{6} = 5:6$ (c) $\dfrac{\text{Meihua's savings}}{\text{Sumin's savings}} = \dfrac{6}{5}$

(d) $\dfrac{\text{Sumin's savings}}{\text{Meihua's savings}} = \dfrac{5}{6}$

10. (a) $\dfrac{\text{Henry's share}}{\text{John's share}} = \dfrac{5}{3}$ (b) $\dfrac{\text{John's share}}{\text{total}} = \dfrac{3}{10}$

11. (a) **3 : 1**   (b) **1 : 3**

(c) $\dfrac{\text{length of string B}}{\text{length of string A}} = \dfrac{1}{3}$

12. (a) **3 : 4**   (b) **4 : 3**

(c) $\dfrac{\text{Minghua's weight}}{\text{Ali's weight}} = \dfrac{4}{3}$

Practice 3A, p. 29, problems 1-5
You can use these problems for more learning tasks, if needed. Answers are on p. 23.

Workbook Exercise 9

(3) Word Problems I (p. 27)

 ➢ Solve word problems involving ratios or the fraction one quantity is of another using pictorial models.

 Since units are not given with a ratio, or when we are given one quantity as a fraction of another, we cannot know the exact amount or measurement of the quantities being compared from just the ratio or the fraction. In word problems we use the ratio along with other information to determine the unit and thus the quantity. We can draw units to represent the relationship between the quantities. For example, there are $\frac{5}{3}$ as many boys as girls. There are 20 more boys than girls. We draw the relationship between the boys and girls as units. We see that there are 2 more units of boys than girls. Since there are 20 more boys than girls, one unit is 10.

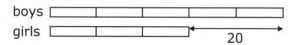

Once we find the value of one unit, we can find the answer to a variety of questions, such as how many children there are in all, or how many boys there are, or how many girls there are.

When discussing the problems in the text, both in this section and in later sections involving word problems and diagramming word problems, you can present the problem to your student and guide him in drawing the diagrams without showing him the diagram in the text ahead of time, rather than just having your student look at the text drawing. He may not draw his diagram in the same way, and this can be a point for discussion and learning. He may approach the problem in a different, but valid way. Allow him the opportunity to explain his solution before assuming that the solution in the text (or in this guide) is the only correct solution or approach.

Keep in mind that diagramming is a problem solving tool, and not the only problem solving tool. If the solution is obvious to your student without a diagram, don't insist that she draw one. But make sure she understands the tool and how to use it.

 Learning Tasks 13-14, p. 27

 13.   1 unit = $60 ÷ 2 = $30
       15 units = $30 × 15 = **$450**

14.   1 unit = 120 ÷ 8 = 15
     3 units = 15 × 3 = **45**

Practice 3A, p. 29, problems 6-7
You can use these problems for more learning tasks, if needed. Answers are on pp. 23-24.

 Workbook Exercise 10

---

(4) Word Problems II (p. 28)

 ➢ Solve word problems involving ratios or the fraction one quantity is of another using pictorial models.

Learning Tasks 15-16, p. 20

15. Note that in this problem, the *number* of Raju's marbles is the same in both ratios, even if the unit is different. So we are finding equivalent ratios where the unit is such that the value in the ratios for Raju's marbles is the same.
    8 : 4 : 5

16. $\dfrac{2}{5}$

 Practice 3A, p. 29, problem 8
You can use this problem for another learning task, if needed. Answers are on p. 24.

 Give your student a problem similar to learning task 15 where the equivalent ratios for *both* quantities need to be found. Have your student draw the diagrams. For example:

The ratio of Peter's marbles to Paul's marbles is 2 : 3 and the ratio of Peter's marbles to Mary's marbles is 5 : 2. What is the ratio of Peter's marbles to Paul's marbles to Mary's marbles?

In this case, the number of Peter's marbles is the same in both ratios, so that is the length that needs to be kept the same. In one ratio, this length is divided into two units; in the other it is divided into five units. To compare all three quantities, we can change the number of units Peter's total is divided up into to a common multiple of 2 and 5, such as 10. We then find the equivalent ratios where the value for Peter's marbles is 10.

2 : 3 = **10** : 15 and **5** : 2 = **10** : 4

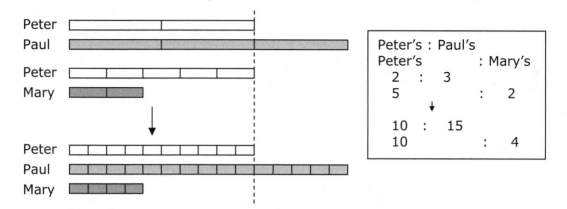

> Give your student a problem similar to learning task 16 where the fraction of one quantity is a *fraction* of another quantity. For example:

$\dfrac{3}{5}$ of Diego's money is $\dfrac{2}{3}$ of Alfonso's money. What fraction of Diego's money is Alfonso's money?

Here, the total of Diego's money is one whole, and the total of Alfonso's money is another whole, and we need to find the fraction of Alfonso's money to Diego's money as the new whole. To solve this problem, we will need to find a common multiple of the two numerators.

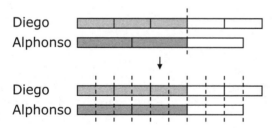

Alphonso's money is $\dfrac{9}{10}$ of Diego's money

 Workbook Exercise 11

Practice (p. 29)

 ➤ Practice problems involving ratios and fractions.

 Up to this point, in both the text and the workbook the diagrams have been given to the student. You may want to guide your student in drawing the diagrams for some of the practice problems, or you can let your student attempt so solve all the problems independently.

 Practice 3A, p. 29

 1. (a) Number of girls = 78 – 60
          = 18
       Number of boys : number of girls
          = 60 : 18
          = **10 : 3**

   (b) $\dfrac{\text{Number of boys}}{\text{Number of girls}} = \dfrac{60}{18} = \dfrac{\textbf{10}}{\textbf{3}}$

2. (a) $\dfrac{\text{Weight of A}}{\text{Weight of B}} = \dfrac{\textbf{3}}{\textbf{4}}$

   (b) $\dfrac{\text{Weight of B}}{\text{Weight of A}} = \dfrac{\textbf{4}}{\textbf{3}}$

3. Mary
    Nancy
    Ann

   (a) $\dfrac{\text{Mary's share}}{\text{Ann's share}} = \dfrac{4}{6} = \dfrac{\textbf{2}}{\textbf{3}}$

   (b) Total money = 15 units
       $\dfrac{\text{Nancy's share}}{\text{total money}} = \dfrac{5}{15} = \dfrac{\textbf{1}}{\textbf{3}}$

4. Betty's height : Jinlan's height = **2 : 3**

   Betty
   Jinlan

5. Minghua's stamps : John's stamps = **3 : 2**

   Minghua
   John

6. girls
    boys   Total units = 4

   (a) number of girls : total number of students = **3 : 4**

   (b) $\dfrac{\text{number of boys}}{\text{total}} = \dfrac{\textbf{1}}{\textbf{4}}$

   (c) 3 units = 27
       1 unit = 27 ÷ 3 = 9
       4 units = 9 × 4 = 36
       There are **36** children.

7. girls   men = 5 units
    boys   women = 8 units

There are 3 more units of women than men.
Total units = 5 + 8 = 13
    3 units = 24
    1 unit = 24 ÷ 3 = 8
13 units = 8 × 13 = 104
There are **104** workers.

8. (a)   men   men : women
            women   3 :   1
                                                   women : children
            women   3 : 5
            children   9 :   3
                                             9 :   3 :   5
            men
            women   men : women : children
            children   = **9 : 3 : 5**

    (b) 5 units = 20
         1 unit = 20 ÷ 5 = 4
         17 units = 4 × 17 = 68
         There are **68** people.

Part 2 – Ratio and Proportion

(1) Ratio and Proportion (pp. 30-32)

➢ Understand proportion.
➢ Express proportion as a fraction or a ratio.
➢ Solve word problems involving direct proportion.

A proportion is a statement that two ratios are equivalent. The statement 3 : 5 = 15 : 25 is a proportion. The statement can also be in the form of fractions. 3 : 5 means that the first quantity is $\frac{3}{5}$ of the second, and 15 : 25 means that the first quantity is $\frac{15}{25}$ of the second. $\frac{3}{5} = \frac{15}{25}$ is a proportion. The relationship between the two expressions is a direct proportion. If 3 increases 5 times, so does 5.

Proportions are used with such things as cooking, scale drawings, and maps. If a recipe calls for 3 cups milk and 5 cups of flour, then we can make 5 times the recipe using 15 cups of milk and 25 cups of flour and those two ingredients would be in the same ratio, so the recipe should turn out. If the scale of a map is 1 cm = 100 km, then a distance of 20 cm on the map would represent an actual distance of 2000 kilometers.

Proportion problems can be represented with unit drawings similarly to ratio problems. The value of the unit changes. If we know the ratio, and the value of one quantity or the difference in the quantities, we can find the value of one unit and from that find the value of the second quantity. For example:

Sand and cement is mixed in a ratio of 3 : 5. So 3 buckets of sand is mixed with 5 buckets of cement. How many buckets of sand would we mix 15 buckets of sand with to get the same proportion? We can draw the ratio, see that 3 units of sand must equal 15, so one unit equals 5, and 5 units of cement equals 25. We need to mix 25 buckets of cement with the 15 buckets of sand to keep the same proportion.

	15
sand	▭▭▭
cement	▭▭▭▭▭

3 units = 15
1 unit = 15 ÷ 3 = 5
5 units = 5 x 5 = 25

We can also find the answer using equivalent fractions: $\frac{3}{5} = \frac{15}{?}$

Pages 30-31

Your student should see that when we increase the number of buckets of cement, the number of buckets of sand should also be increased by the same factor. The amount of cement and sand are in proportion.

$$\frac{\text{Number of buckets of cement}}{\text{Number of buckets of sand}} \text{ is always equivalent to } \frac{5}{3}.$$

$\dfrac{5}{3} = \dfrac{\mathbf{50}}{30}$ $\dfrac{5}{3} = \dfrac{30}{\mathbf{18}}$

Discuss other examples. For example:

- $\dfrac{\text{weight on the moon}}{\text{weight on earth}} = \dfrac{1}{6}$

  Have your student find out what her weight would be if she were on the moon.
- Use a map, discuss the scale on the map, and have your student estimate some actual distances between cities or other features using the map and a ruler and applying the concept of proportions.

Learning Tasks 1-3, pp. 31-32

1.   (a) **8; 32**   (b) **1 : 2**

2.   (a) **1 : 3**   (b) $3 \times 6\,\ell = \mathbf{18\,\ell}$ (c) $15\,\ell \div 3 = \mathbf{5\,\ell}$

3.   (a)   3 units = 12 ℓ (b) 5 units = 10 ℓ
          1 unit = 12 ÷ 3   1 unit = 10 ÷ 5
               = 4 ℓ = 2 ℓ
          2 units = 4 × 2   3 units = 2 × 3
               = **8 ℓ**   = **6 ℓ**

Workbook Exercise 12

Practice (p. 33)

 ➢ Practice problems involving ratio and proportion.

 Your student may be able to do this practice independently, or you can use some of the problems as learning tasks.

Practice 3B, p. 33

 1. (a) weight of sugar : weight of flour = 20 : 50 = **2 : 5**

(b) 2 units = 80 g
1 unit = 80 ÷ 2 = 40 g
5 units = 40 × 5 = 200 g
200 g of flour are needed.

2. (a) number of boys : number of girls = **4 : 3**

(b) 3 units = 42
1 unit = 42 ÷ 3 = 14
4 units = 14 × 4 = 56
There are **56** boy scouts.

US› 3. (a) 1 unit = 3 cups
5 units = 3 × 5 = 15 cups
She will use **15 cups** of flour.

(b) 5 units = 20 cups
1 unit = 20 ÷ 5 = 4 cups
She will use **4 cups** of milk.

3d› 3. (a) 1 unit = 3 cups
5 units = 3 × 5 = 15 cups
She will use **15 cups** of water.

(b) 5 units = 20 cups
1 unit = 20 ÷ 5 = 4 cups
She will use **4 cups** of rice.

US› 4. 3 units = 12 gal
1 unit = 12 ÷ 3 = 4 gal
2 units = 4 × 2 = 8 gal
He used **8 gal** of blue paint.

US› 4. 3 units = 12 liters
1 unit = 12 ÷ 3 = 4 liters
2 units = 4 × 2 = 8 liters
He used **8 liters** of blue paint.

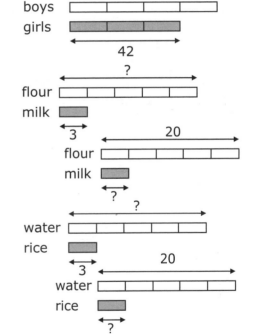
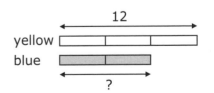

5. 2 units = 6 cups
    1 unit = 6 ÷ 2 = 3 cups
    14 units = 3 × 14 = 42 cups
    She made **42 cups** of drink.

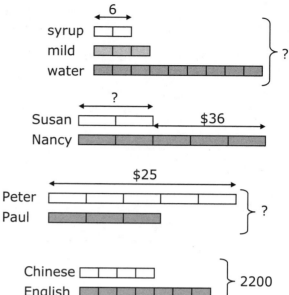

6. 3 units = $36
    1 unit = $36 ÷ 3 = $12
    2 units = $12 × 2 = $24
    Susan received **$24**.

7. 5 units = $25
    1 unit = $25 ÷ 5 = $5
    8 units = $5 × 8 = $40
    They have **$40** altogether.

8. 11 units = 2200
    1 unit = 2200 ÷ 11 = 200
    7 units = 200 × 7 = 1400
    There are **1400** English books.

9. 15 units = 60 cm
    1 unit = 60 ÷ 15 = 4 cm
    4 units = 4 × 4 = 16 cm
    The shortest side is **16 cm**.

Part 3 – Changing Ratios

(1) Finding the New Ratio (pp. 34-36)

 ➢ Solve word problems involving before and after situations where the ratio changes.

 A changing ratio problem involves a "before" situation and an "after" situation in which the ratio of the two quantities has changed. These problems can be illustrated by drawing separate diagrams for each situation. Generally, with these problems, as with the ratio and proportion problems already seen in this unit, we will need to find the value of a unit, either in the before situation or in the after situation. Care should be taken to relate the two diagrams to each other, since this relationship will be used to find the value of a unit. If one quantity does not change, this should be shown in the diagram. If both quantities do change, the amount by which they change should be shown.

You can give your student the problems in the learning tasks and guide him in diagramming them before studying the diagrams in the text.

(Note that I am including learning task 3 in this section even though the workbook exercise arrow is after learning task 2.)

 Page 34
Discuss this page with your student. She should notice that in both situations Henry's bar is the same length. In the first drawing, it is divided up into 3 units. In the second, it must be divided up into 6 units. So each unit in the second drawing should be half that in the first drawing. Once that is determined, then Peter's bar in the second drawing can be drawn to be 5 units long, and it can be seen that one of those units is how much longer it is than in the first drawing, so 1 unit = 8. From that, we can find the answers to the questions.

 Peter had $4 \times 8 = $ **32** stamps at first. He now has $5 \times 8 = $ **40** stamps.

 Learning Tasks 1-3, pp. 35-36
In the first two problems, a change occurs in the amount and the student needs to find a new ratio. The amount of the change is not related to a unit in each of these problems — we need to find the initial quantities, the new quantities, and then the new ratios. In the third problem, we don't need to find the actual amounts, since we are told a fraction by which the amounts change.

 1.   New ratio = **1 : 2**

2.   1 unit = 40 ÷ 2 = 20
      Before: Number of (**US**› Susan's, **3d**› Sulin's) books = 3 × 20 = **60**
      New ratio is 48 : 60 = **4 : 5**

3.   New ratio = **2 : 5**

 Workbook Exercise 13

In the first problem in the workbook exercise 13, the student can find the amount before, then the amount after, and then the new ratio. This solution is shown in the workbook solution section of this guide. In the second problem, no amounts are given, but since we are given the fraction of the first amount that changes, we can find the new ratio.

If your student solves the first problem by finding the actual amount you may want to discuss how the first problem can be solved similarly to the second problem. How can we change the units for Suhua's stickers so that she gives Meili one fourth of the units? If we use the equivalent ratio 12 : 28, Suhua can give Meili one fourth of the units, or 7 of the 28. So Meili's units become 12 + 7 = 19, and Suhua's units become 28 – 7 = 21, and the new ratio is 19 : 21. In this solution, we don't need the information that Suhua has 32 more stickers than Meili.

---

(2) Finding Amounts using Changing Ratios (pp. 36-37)

 ➢ Solve word problems involving before and after situations where the ratio changes.

 Learning Tasks 4-6, pp. 36-37
In these problems, we are given the ratios for both situations, and one quantity. We need to use this information to find the value of a unit in either the before situation or the after situation. It is important to find the relationship between the units in both situations.

 4.   If they have an equal amount of money after Susan gave $20 to Mary, Susan must have given Mary half the difference in their original amounts. Since the difference is 2 units, she gave Mary 1 unit, so 1 unit = $20.
      3 units = $20 × 3 = **$60**

5.   1 unit = $60
      4 units = $60 × 4 = $240
      He has **$240**.

6.   We need to keep track of the money spent, which is the amount removed from the two bars before. The difference between these is 1 unit. If this is hard to visualize, superimpose the diagram for the after situation on top of the diagram for the before situation by drawing the units on top of the first two bars and marking the amount taken away for each.
1 unit after = $25 – $18 = $7
John's original money = (2 × $7) + $25 = **$39**

 Workbook Exercise 14

Practice (p. 38)

   ➤   Practice problems involving changing ratios.

 In diagramming changing ratio problems, it is sometimes easier to draw the diagram for the after situation first, if a ratio is given for that situation and not for the before situation (other than equal amounts). In the solutions to these problems, this has been done for problems 3 and 4. You may want to discuss one of these problems with your student, either before or after he has worked on it independently.

 Practice 3C (p. 38)

   1.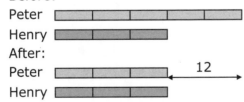

1 unit = 6
boys = 4 units = 6 × 4 = 24
girls = 3 units = 6 × 3 = 18

2 girls join the choir.
Number of girls becomes 18 + 2 = 20
New ratio of boys : girls = 24 : 20 = **6 : 5**

2.   Before:

Peter
Henry
After:
Peter   12
Henry

2 unit = $12
1 unit = $12 ÷ 2 = $6
Peter had 5 units at first.
5 units = $6 x 5 = $30
Peter had **$30** at first.

3.   After:
Ali
Samy   15
Before:
Ali
Samy

1 unit = $15
Both had 6 units at first.
6 units = $15 x 6 = $90
Both had **$90** at first.

4. After:

Sally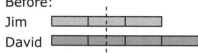

Susan

Before:

Sally

Susan

1 unit = $24 – $15 = $9
Sally originally had 4 units + $15
(4 x $9) + $15 = $36 + $15 = $51
Both had **$51** at first.

or: Susan had 3 units + $24
(3 x $9) + $24 = $51

5. Before: After:

Jim   Jim

David   David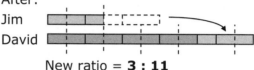

New ratio = **3 : 11**

6. Before:

Meili

Sulin

After:

Meili   12

Sulin

(a) 3 units = 12
1 unit = 12 ÷ 3 = 4
Sulin had 2 units.
2 units = 4 x 2 = 8
Sulin had **8** books.

(b) Meili now has 4 x 4 = 16 books
Sulin adds 5 books.
Sulin then has 8 + 5 = 13 books
New ratio = **16 : 13**

7. A   12

    B

(a)   4 unit = 12
1 unit = 12 ÷ 4 = 3
10 units = 3 × 10 = 30
There are **30** marbles
altogether.

(b) A has 3 × 3 = 9 marbles
B has 3 × 7 = 21 marbles
After moving 3 from A to B,
A has 9 – 3 = 6 marbles and
B has 21 + 3 = 24 marbles.
New ratio = 6 : 24 = **1 : 4**

8. John

    Sumin
                20

$\frac{1}{2}$ unit = $20

1 unit = $40

(a) 2 units = $40 × 2 = $80
Sumin had **$80**.

(b) 5 units = $40 × 5 = $200
John had **$200** at first.

Review

Reviews in *Primary Mathematics* cover material from all previous levels. If your student is new to *Primary Mathematics* and has difficulty with some of the topics in the reviews, you may wish to review them with the texts from Primary Mathematics 4A-5B. Topics that may cause problems are fractions (4A covers adding and subtraction related fractions, mixed numbers and improper fractions, multiplying a fraction by a whole number, 5A covers addition and subtraction of unrelated fractions and mixed numbers, multiplication of fractions, and division of a fraction by a whole number), area and volume (4A covers area and perimeter of composite figures, 4B covers volume, 5A covers area of a triangle, and 5B covers finding volume by displacement), order of operations, unknown angles (covered in 5A), and percentage, average, rate and ratio (all covered in 5B).

You may wish to have your student work through all three reviews (two in the text and one in the workbook) now, or you can to assign several pages of review once a week or part of a page daily for more continuous review as you proceed with the next units.

The reviews in the text tend to be a bit more challenging than the reviews in the workbook, and the problems can be good opportunities for discussion of concepts and solutions. If your student has difficulty with a problem, have him explain his reasoning and approach before simply giving him the correct answers so that you can see exactly what type of misunderstanding he has.

There are usually several ways to solve a problem. The solutions in this guide show only one or two approaches. Sometime one approach is shown for one problem and a different one with another, similar problem, to help you be aware of the different approaches without giving multiple solutions for each problem. Your student may find a different, valid way to solve some of the problems. You can compare and discuss different solutions.

 Review A, pp. 39-42

1.   (a) **40,580**   (b) **2,070,000**

2.   (a) **six hundred thousand, two hundred thirty**
     (b) **eight million, five thousand**

3.   **109,000**

4.   **$214,000**

5.   (a) **45**   (b) **1000**

6.   (a) $12 - \underline{4 \div 2} + 6$
         $= \underline{12 - 2} + 6$
         $= \underline{10 + 6}$
         $= \mathbf{16}$

     (b) $24 + \underline{6 \times 7} \div 3$
         $= 24 + \underline{42 \div 3}$
         $= \underline{24 + 14}$
         $= \mathbf{38}$

(c)　$(4+8) \times 3 \div 4$
　　　$= \underline{12 \times 3} \div 4$
　　　$= \underline{36 \div 4}$
　　　$= \mathbf{9}$

(d)　$25 - (6 + \underline{9 \times 2}) + 5$
　　　$= 25 - (\underline{6 + 18}) + 5$
　　　$= \underline{25 - 24} + 5$
　　　$= \underline{1 + 5}$
　　　$= \mathbf{6}$

7.　32: 1, 2, 4, 8, 16, 32　　64: 1, 2, 4, 8, 16, 32, 64　　76: 1, 2, 4, 19, 76
Common factors: **1, 2, or 4**

8.　Multiples of 8: 8, 16, 24, 32....
24 is a multiple of 8.

9.　(a)
$$\begin{array}{r} 8.875 \\ 8\overline{)7.000} \\ \underline{6\,4} \\ 60 \\ \underline{56} \\ 40 \\ \underline{40} \\ 0 \end{array}$$

$\dfrac{7}{8} = \mathbf{0.875}$

(b)
$$\begin{array}{r} 0.666 \\ 3\overline{)2.000} \\ \underline{1\,8} \\ 20 \\ \underline{18} \\ 20 \\ \underline{18} \\ 2 \end{array}$$

$\dfrac{2}{3} \approx 0.67$

$4\dfrac{2}{3} \approx \mathbf{4.67}$

10.　(a)　$0.006 = \dfrac{6}{1000} = \dfrac{\mathbf{3}}{\mathbf{500}}$

(b)　$1.8 = 1\dfrac{8}{10} = \mathbf{1}\dfrac{\mathbf{4}}{\mathbf{5}}$

11.　(a)　$3 : 6 = \mathbf{9} : 18$　(x 3)

(b)　$14 : 21 = 2 : \mathbf{3}$　($\div$ 7)

(c)　$20 : 8 : 4 = \mathbf{10} : \mathbf{4} : 2$　($\div$ 2)

(d)　$\dfrac{2}{3} = \mathbf{2} : 3$

12.　$\dfrac{\text{2 packets}}{\text{15 cakes}} = \dfrac{\text{10 packets}}{\text{? cakes}}$　$2 \times 5 = 10$, so $15 \times 5 = \mathbf{75}$ cakes

or:

packets ▭▭   10

cakes ▭▭▭▭▭▭▭▭▭▭▭▭▭▭▭
　　　　　　　?

2 units = 10
1 unit = 5
15 units = 5×15 = 75

13.　(a)　$26 + x = 26 + 6$
　　　　　$= \mathbf{32}$

(b)　$32 - x = 32 - 6$
　　　　$= \mathbf{26}$

(c)　$7x = 7 \times 6$
　　　$= \mathbf{42}$

(d)　$\dfrac{8x}{3} = \dfrac{8 \times 6}{3}$
　　　　$= 8 \times 2$
　　　　$= \mathbf{16}$

(e)　$3x + 7 = (3 \times 6) + 7$
　　　　　$= 18 + 7$
　　　　　$= \mathbf{25}$

(f)　$2x^2 = 2 \times 6 \times 6$
　　　　$= \mathbf{72}$

14. (a) $14y - 5y + y = (14 - 5 + 1)y$
$= \mathbf{10y}$

(b) $10y + 15 - 3y - 8$
$= (10 - 3)y + 15 - 8$
$= \mathbf{7y + 7}$

15. Total oranges in big boxes $= 60 \times 2 = 120$
Total oranges in 2 big and 1 small box $= 120 + 48 = 168$
Average number of oranges in each box $= \dfrac{168}{3} = \mathbf{56}$

16. Total weight of 2 of the men $= 54.9 \times 2 = 109.8$ kg
Weight of third man = total weight of 3 men – weight of 2 men
$= 164.4$ kg $- 109.8$ kg $= \mathbf{54.6}$ **kg**

17. Total number of T-shirts sold $= 200 - 20 = 180$
Total money made from sale $= 180 \times \$5 = \$900$
The profit was $360.
Cost = Sale – Profit $= \$900 - \$360 = \$540$
Cost price for 1 shirt $= \dfrac{\$540}{200} = \mathbf{\$2.70}$

18. 5 oranges cost $2.
1 orange costs $\dfrac{2}{5}$.

100 oranges cost $\$\dfrac{2}{5} \times 100 = \$2 \times 20 = \$40$

Amount of money still needed $= \$40 - \$35.50 = \mathbf{\$4.50}$

19. $\dfrac{1}{2}$ of a cake is $2 \times \dfrac{1}{4}$ of a cake.

$\dfrac{1}{4}$ of a cake weighs $\dfrac{1}{2}$ kg.

$\dfrac{1}{2}$ of a cake weighs $2 \times \dfrac{1}{2}$ kg $= \mathbf{1}$ **kg**

20. Fraction of water remaining $= 1 - \dfrac{3}{8} = \dfrac{5}{8}$

Amount of water left $= \dfrac{5}{8} \times \dfrac{1}{2} \, \ell = \dfrac{\mathbf{5}}{\mathbf{16}} \, \ell$

21. Fraction of cookies left $= 1 - \dfrac{3}{4} = \dfrac{1}{4}$

$\dfrac{1}{4}$ of the cookies $= 20$ cookies

$\dfrac{4}{4}$ of the cookies $= 20 \times 4 = \mathbf{80}$ cookies

22.

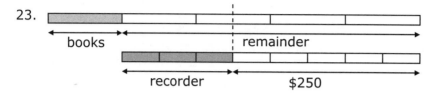

?   500 ml

◻ = 1 unit
1 unit = 500 ml
10 units = 500 × 10 = 5,000 ml = **5 ℓ**

23.

books   remainder

recorder $250

(a)   Fraction left = $\dfrac{5}{8} \times \dfrac{4}{5} = \dfrac{\mathbf{1}}{\mathbf{2}}$

(b)   Amount at first = 2 × $250 = **$500**

24.

red   yellow   pink

There is 1 unit more pink roses than red.
1 unit = 24
4 units = 24 × 4 = 96
There are **96** roses.

25. $\dfrac{\text{Jim's weight}}{\text{Eva's weight}} = \dfrac{\mathbf{5}}{\mathbf{4}}$

26. (a) Sumin's savings : Meili's savings = **3 : 1**
    (b) 2 units = $20
        1 unit = $20 ÷ 2 = $10
        Meili saves **$10**.

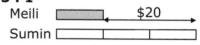

Meili $20
Sumin

27.   swordtails
      angelfish   25
      guppies

(a) swordtails : angelfish : guppies
          2 :   3
          1 :   4
     = 2 :   8
       2 :   3   :   8

(b) 5 more units of guppies than angelfish, 13 units altogether.
     5 units = 25
     1 unit = 25 ÷ 5 = 5
     13 units = 5 × 13 = 65
     There are **65** fish.

28. Henry has 2 more units than Peter.
John has 6 units.
2 units = $80
1 unit = $80 ÷ 2 = $40
6 units = $40 × 6 = $240
John has **$240**.

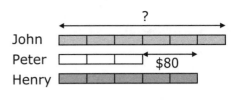

29. Osman's money does not change.
Ratio of Aziz to Osman at first = 2 : 1 = 6 : 3
Ratio changes to 4 : 3. So Aziz loses 2 units.
2 units = $10
1 unit = $10 ÷ 2 = $5
6 units = $5 × 6 = $30
3 units = $5 × 3 = $15
At first, Aziz had **$30** and Osman had **$15**.

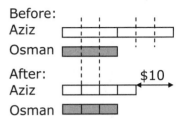

30. (a)   1 min ⟶ 80 words
10 min ⟶ 80 × 10
           = 800 words
He can type **800** words in
10 min.

(b)   80 words ⟶ 1 min
1 word ⟶ $\frac{1}{80}$ min

2000 words ⟶ $\frac{1}{80}$ × 2000 min
              = 25 min
It will take him **25 min**.

31. 100 g ⟶ $0.45
600 g ⟶ $0.45 × 6 = **$2.70**

32. Cost for first 10 words = $9
Cost for remaining 6 words = $0.60 × 6 = $3.60
Total cost = $9 + $3.60 = **$12.60**

33. **5** faces (3 rectangular and 2 triangular)

34. **A** and **D**

35. Perimeter = 8 + 3 + 3 + 3 + 8 + 5 + 3 + 8 + 3 cm
             = (8 × 3) + (5 × 3) + 5 cm
             = 24 + 15 + 5 cm
             = **44 cm**

36. The base of the triangle is 20 − 8 = 12 cm, and its corresponding height is 8 cm.
Area = area of square + area of triangle
= (8 × 8) + ($\frac{1}{2}$ × 12 × 8) cm^2
= 64 × 48 cm^2
= **112 cm^2**

Review B, pp. 43-46

1. (a) $\dfrac{5}{8}$

   (b) $\dfrac{1}{2} \times \dfrac{3}{5} + \dfrac{1}{2} \times \dfrac{1}{5} = \dfrac{3}{10} + \dfrac{1}{10} = \dfrac{4}{10} = \dfrac{2}{5}$

2. $\dfrac{6}{5} = 1\dfrac{1}{5}$

3. (a) $3\dfrac{1}{3} = \dfrac{9}{3} + \dfrac{1}{3} = \dfrac{10}{3}$

   (b) $\dfrac{7}{5} = \dfrac{5}{5} + \dfrac{2}{5} = 1 + \dfrac{2}{5}$

4. (a) **500**
   (b) **1000**
   (c) **0.49**
   (d) **0.024**

5. **6**

6. (a) any multiple of **36**

   (b) $\dfrac{1}{3} + \dfrac{1}{4} + \dfrac{1}{9} = \dfrac{12}{36} + \dfrac{9}{36} + \dfrac{4}{36} = \dfrac{25}{36}$

7. **0.83**

8. $\dfrac{3}{5}$ is smaller than $\dfrac{3}{4}$ (same numerator, larger denominator).

$\dfrac{3}{5} = \dfrac{18}{30}, \ \dfrac{5}{6} = \dfrac{25}{30}$ so $\dfrac{3}{5}$ is smaller than $\dfrac{5}{6}$

$\dfrac{3}{5} = \dfrac{9}{15}, \ \dfrac{2}{3} = \dfrac{10}{15}$ so $\dfrac{3}{5}$ is smaller than $\dfrac{2}{3}$

$\dfrac{3}{5}$ is smallest.

9. (a) $1 \ell = 1,000$ ml

    $\dfrac{2}{5} \ell = \dfrac{2}{5} \times 1000$ ml $= 400$ ml

    $1\dfrac{2}{5} \ell =$ **1400 ml**

   (b) 1 m = 100 cm

    $\dfrac{1}{4}$ m $= \dfrac{1}{4} \times 100$ cm $= 25$ cm

    $1\dfrac{1}{4}$ m = **125 cm**

10. (a) 1.72 km = 1.72 × 1000 m
               = **1720 m**

   (b) 125 min = 120 min + 5 min
                = **2 h 5 min**

11. 10:30 a.m + 5 h 40 min = 3:30 p.m. + 30 min + 10 min = **4:10 p.m.**

12. (a) **328,000**
    (b) **5000**
    (c) **240,000**
    (d) **160**

13. Each division is 0.25 ℓ. Level is close to but slightly less than 1.8 ℓ.
1.7 ℓ is the best estimate.

14. Each longer division is 1 kg. The pointer is closer to 48 kg than 47.5 kg.
47.9 kg is the best estimate.

15. (a) Her mother is $12 + m$ years.
In 5 years she will be $12 + m + 5 = \mathbf{17 + m}$ years
(b) $17 + m = 17 + 20 = \mathbf{37}$ years

16. (a) Perimeter $= 2 \times (10 + x)$ cm $= \mathbf{(20 + 2x)\ cm}$
(b) $20 + 2x = 20 + (2 \times 6) = 20 + 12 = \mathbf{32\ cm}$

17. Total students present $= 38 - 4 - 2 = 32$
Fraction present $= \dfrac{32}{38} = \dfrac{\mathbf{16}}{\mathbf{19}}$

US› 18. Connor's money = Joe's money $- \$10 = \$35 - \$10 = \$25$
Tyler's money = half of Connor's money $= \dfrac{1}{2} \times \$25 = \$12.50$
Total money $= \$35 + \$25 + \$12.50 = \mathbf{\$72.50}$

3d› 18. Rahman's money = Ali's money $- \$10 = \$35 - \$10 = \$25$
Samy's money = half of Rahman's money $= \dfrac{1}{2} \times \$25 = \$12.50$
Total money $= \$35 + \$25 + \$12.50 = \mathbf{\$72.50}$

19. Cost of 4 mangoes $= \$8.80$
Cost of 1 mango $\quad= \$8.80 \div 4 = \$2.20$
Cost of 5 mangoes $= \$2.20 \times 5 = \$11.00$
Cost of 3 kg of (**US›** cherries, **3d›** rambutans) $+$ 5 mangoes $= \$15.50$
Cost of 3 kg of cherries (rambutans) $= \$15.50 - \$11.00 = \$4.50$
Cost of 1 kg of cherries (rambutans) $= \$4.50 \div 3 = \mathbf{\$1.50}$

20. Total weight of 4 sacks $= 18 \times 4 = 72$ kg
Total weight of 3 sacks $= 17.50 \times 3 = 52.5$ kg
Weight of fourth sack = weight of all 4 $-$ weight of 3 sacks
$\qquad\qquad = 72$ kg $- 52.5$ kg $= \mathbf{19.5\ kg}$

21. Total used $= \dfrac{1}{4} + \left(\dfrac{1}{5} \times \dfrac{3}{4} \right) = \dfrac{1}{4} + \dfrac{3}{20} = \dfrac{5}{20} + \dfrac{3}{20} = \dfrac{8}{20} = \dfrac{2}{5}$ kg

22. Fraction of butter cookies $= \dfrac{1}{3} = \dfrac{5}{15} = 5$ units
Fraction of cherry cookies $= \dfrac{2}{5} = \dfrac{6}{15} = 5$ units
Fraction of chocolate cookies $= \dfrac{15}{15} - \dfrac{5}{15} - \dfrac{6}{15} = \dfrac{4}{15} = 4$ units

There is $\dfrac{1}{15}$, or 1 unit more cherry cookies than butter cookies.
1 unit $= 30$ cookies
4 units $= 30 \times 4 = 120$
There are **120** chocolate cookies.

23. 2 units = $9
   1 unit = $9 ÷ 2 = $4.50
   cost of noodles + cost of drink = $4.50
   cost of drink = $4.50 − cost of noodles
   　　　　= $4.50 − $3.60 = **$0.90**

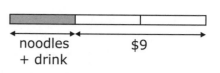

noodles
+ drink $9

24. Fraction read on Tuesday $= \dfrac{2}{5} = \dfrac{8}{20} = 8$ units

   Fraction left $= \dfrac{1}{4} = \dfrac{5}{20} = 5$ units

   Fraction read on Monday $= \dfrac{20}{20} - \dfrac{8}{20} - \dfrac{5}{20} = \dfrac{7}{20} = 7$ units

   　7 units = 42
   　1 unit = 42 ÷ 7 = 6
   20 units = 6 × 20 = 120
   There are **120** pages.

25.   **US›**
   Ryan
   Juan
   　　☐ = 1 unit

   $80
   $500
   3d›
   Raju
   Samy

   (a) Juan (Samy) has 5 units; Ryan (Raju) started with 3 units + $80.
   　8 units = $500 − $80 = $420
   　1 unit = $420 ÷ 8 = $52.50
   　5 units = $52.50 × 5 = $262.50
   (b) Juan (Samy) has **$262.50**
   　3 units + $80 = (3 × $52.50) + $80 = $157.50 + $80 = $237.50
   　Ryan (Raju) had **$237.50** at first.

26. 4 units = 24
   1 unit = 24 ÷ 4 = 6
   He used **6 cups** milk.

flour
milk   24

27. beef pies : chicken pies : fruit pies = 36 : 72 : 54 = **2 : 4 : 3**   (÷ 18)

28. 14 units = 84 in.
   　1 unit = 6 in.
   　9 units = 6 × 9 = 54 in.
   The longer piece is **54** in. long.

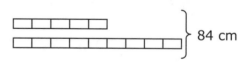

84 cm

29. (a) Fraction Carol received $= \dfrac{5}{11}$

   (b) 3 units = $15
   　1 unit = $15 ÷ 3 = $5
   　4 units = $5 × 4 = $20
   　Angela received **$20**.

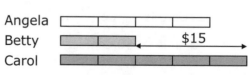

Angela
Betty $15
Carol

30. children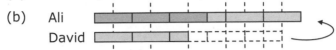
    adults

    men   women

    men : women : children = **5 : 3 : 4**

31. (a) Ali's money : David's money = **3 : 5**

    (b) Ali
         David

    Ali's money : David's money = **11 : 5**

32. Area of square = $5 \times 4 = 20$ cm^2

    Area of A = $\frac{1}{2} \times 2 \times 4 = 4$ cm^2

    Area of B = $\frac{1}{2} \times 3 \times 3 = 4\frac{1}{2}$ cm^2

    Area of C = $\frac{1}{2} \times 5 \times 1 = 2\frac{1}{2}$ cm^2

    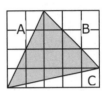

    Shaded area = area of square – area of A – area of B – area of C

    $= 20 - 4 - 4\frac{1}{2} - 2\frac{1}{2} = $ **9 cm^2**

33. (a) Area = area of triangle + area of rectangle

    $= \frac{1}{2} \times 12 \times 16 + 10 \times 20$ cm^2

    $= 96 + 200$ cm^2

    $= $ **296 cm^2**

    (b) Perimeter = $12 + 16 + 10 + 20 + 10$ cm = **68 cm**

34. Perimeter of P = $(2 \times$ length of P$) + (2 \times$ width of P$)$

    $32 = 2 \times 12 + (2 \times$ width of P$)$

    $32 = 24 + (2 \times$ width of P$)$

    $32 - 24 = (2 \times$ width of P$)$

    $8 = 2 \times$ width of P

    width of P $= \frac{1}{2} \times 8 = 4$ cm

    Area of P = length of P $\times$ width of P = 12 cm $\times$ 4 cm = 48 cm^2 = area of Q

    Area of Q = length of Q $\times$ width of Q

    $48 = $ length of Q $\times 6$

    length of Q = $48 \div 6 = 8$ cm

    Perimeter of Q = $(2 \times$ length of Q$) + (2 \times$ width of Q$)$

    $= (2 \times 8) + (2 \times 6) = 16 + 12 = $ **28 cm**

📖 **Workbook Review 1**

Unit 4 – Percentage

Part 1 – Part of a Whole as Percentage

(1) Fraction as Percentage (pp. 47-50)

➤ Express a part of a whole as a percentage.

In *Primary Mathematics 5B*, students learned to express a part of a whole as a percentage. This is reviewed in this section.

A percentage is simply a specific type of fraction, one where the denominator is 100. 1 percent, which is written as 1%, is one part out of a hundred, or $\frac{1}{100}$.

55% means 55 out of 100, or $\frac{55}{100}$, or 55%.

Other fractions are also parts of a whole. $\frac{11}{25}$ is 11 out of 25. To convert to a percentage, we can find the equivalent fraction with a denominator of 100. $\frac{11}{25} = \frac{44}{100} = 44\%$. Instead of dividing the whole into 25 parts, we divide it into 100 parts. Each of the original parts is subdivided into 4 parts, so there are 4 times as many 1% parts.

We can also convert a fraction to a percentage by thinking of it as a fraction of the whole, with the whole being 100%. 1 = 100%.

$$\frac{11}{25} \text{ of the whole} = \frac{11}{25} \text{ of } 100\% = \frac{11}{25} \times 100\% = \frac{11 \times 100}{25}\% = \frac{11 \times \cancel{100}^4}{\cancel{25}_1} = 44\%$$

➤ Ask your student to tell you what a percentage is. A percentage is a specific fraction where the denominator is 100. Instead of being written as a fraction, it can be written as the number in the numerator followed by the percent symbol, %. $\frac{10}{100} = 10\%$. Discuss ways percentages are used, e.g. percent score on a test, percent humidity, percent chance of rain...

Learning Task 1, p. 48
(Save p. 47 until after learning task 5).

(a) The larger rectangle is the whole. 13 out of 50 squares are shaded. The whole can be divided into 100 parts instead. If it is, then 26 out of 50 of the smaller units, which are half the size of the original units, are shaded. The new fraction is an equivalent fraction of the old one.

$$\frac{13}{50} = \frac{26}{100} = \mathbf{26\%}$$

(b) The larger rectangle again is the whole. 120 out of 300 parts are shaded. The whole can be divided into 100 parts instead. Each new part would be three times the size of the old part, since $300 \div 3 = 100$. So $120 \div 3$, or 40 of the new parts would be shaded. Since both the denominator (total parts) and numerator (number of parts shaded) are divided by the same number, we are finding an equivalent fraction with a denominator of 100. This can be written as a percentage.

$$\frac{120}{300} = \frac{40}{100} = \mathbf{40\%}$$

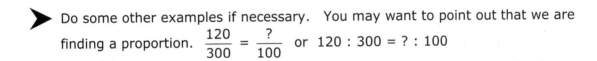

Do some other examples if necessary. You may want to point out that we are finding a proportion. $\frac{120}{300} = \frac{?}{100}$ or $120 : 300 = ? : 100$

 Learning Tasks 2-3, pp. 48-49

2. (a) $\dfrac{6}{100} = \mathbf{6\%}$ (b) $\dfrac{2}{10} = \dfrac{20}{100} = \mathbf{20\%}$ (c) $\dfrac{3}{50} = \dfrac{6}{100} = \mathbf{6\%}$

(d) $\dfrac{4}{25} = \dfrac{16}{100} = \mathbf{16\%}$ (e) $\dfrac{18}{200} = \dfrac{9}{100} = \mathbf{9\%}$ (f) $\dfrac{75}{300} = \dfrac{25}{100} = \mathbf{25\%}$

3. (a) $\dfrac{24}{50} = \dfrac{48}{100} = \mathbf{48\%}$ (b) $\dfrac{16}{25} = \dfrac{64}{100} = \mathbf{64\%}$ (c) $\dfrac{30}{75} = \dfrac{10}{25} = \dfrac{40}{100} = \mathbf{40\%}$

(d) $\dfrac{180}{600} = \dfrac{30}{100} = \mathbf{30\%}$ (e) $\dfrac{60}{150} = \dfrac{4}{10} = \dfrac{40}{100} = \mathbf{40\%}$ (f) $\dfrac{15}{250} = \dfrac{3}{50} = \dfrac{6}{100} = \mathbf{6\%}$

Learning Task 4, p. 49

$\frac{3}{5}$ is shown as a shaded part of a fraction bar, then as a fraction on a number line from 0 to 1. The fraction bar is a whole. Since 100% = 1 whole, we can draw a "percent ruler" with the same length as the whole fraction bar. If necessary, remind your student that a fraction *of* a number is the same as the fraction *times* that number. If the length of the whole bar is 100, then the length of the 3 shaded units is

$$\frac{3}{5} \text{ of the whole} = \frac{3}{5} \text{ of } 100\% = \frac{3}{5} \times 100\% = \frac{3 \times 100}{5}\% = \frac{3 \times \cancel{100}^{20}}{\cancel{5}_1} = 60\%$$

Tell your student that for mental math purposes, it is easier to simplify the fraction first and then multiply, than to do $\frac{3 \times 100}{5} = \frac{300}{5}$ and then divide 5 into 300.

➤ You may want to relate this process to unit bar diagrams that the student has been using for fractions, ratios, and proportion. The bar is divided into 5 units, and 3 units are shaded to show $\frac{3}{5}$. If the whole is 100, what is the value of the 3 units?

5 units = 100

1 unit $= 100 \div 5 = \dfrac{100}{5}$

3 units $= 3 \times \dfrac{100}{5} = \dfrac{3}{5} \times 100 = 60$

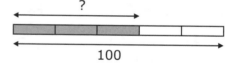

➤ Have your student express other fifths as percentages as well. She should eventually memorize these fraction-percentage equivalents.

$$\frac{1}{5} = 20\%; \quad \frac{2}{5} = 40\%; \quad \frac{3}{5} = 60\%; \quad \frac{4}{5} = 80\%; \quad \frac{5}{5} = 100\%$$

 Learning Task 5, p. 49

☑ $\dfrac{1}{8} \times 100\% = \dfrac{1}{\cancel{8}_2} \times \cancel{100}^{25}\% = \dfrac{25}{2}\% = \mathbf{12.5\%} \text{ or } \mathbf{12\frac{1}{2}\%}$

Percentages do not have to be whole numbers. They can be decimals or fraction percents. Half of a percent is half of one of the 100 1% units.

> Have your student express the other eighths as percentages as well. Some of them are also fourths.

$$\frac{1}{8} = 12.5\%; \quad \frac{2}{8} = \frac{1}{4} = 25\%; \quad \frac{3}{8} = 37.5\% \quad \frac{4}{8} = \frac{2}{4} = \frac{1}{2} = 50\%;$$

$$\frac{5}{8} = 62.5\%; \quad \frac{6}{8} = \frac{3}{4} = 75\%; \quad \frac{7}{8} = 87.5\%; \quad \frac{8}{8} = 100\%$$

He should memorize the percentage equivalent for $\frac{1}{8}$. From that and those for fourths he can mentally find the others. For example:

$$\frac{5}{8} = \frac{1}{2} + \frac{1}{8} = 50\% + 12.5\%$$

 Page 47

This shows both methods for finding the percentage from a fraction.

 60% of the students are girls.

 Learning Task 6, p. 50

 6.   (a) $\frac{1}{4} \times 100\% =$ **25%**   (b) $\frac{1}{5} \times 100\% =$ **20%**   (c) $\frac{3}{4} \times 100\% =$ **75%**

     (d) $\frac{4}{5} \times 100\% =$ **80%**   (e) $\frac{3}{8} \times 100\% =$ **37.5%**   (f) $\frac{7}{10} \times 100\% =$ **70%**

 Workbook Exercise 15

---

(2) Percentage, Fractions, and Decimals (p. 50)

   ➢ Express a percentage as a fraction in its simplest form.
  ➢ Express a percentage as a decimal.

 In *Primary Mathematics 5B*, students learned to express a percentage as a fraction in its simplest form or a decimal. This is reviewed here.

To express a percentage as a fraction in its simplest form, we first express the percentage as a fraction with a denominator of 100, then we simplify the fraction.

$$25\% = \frac{25}{100} = \frac{1}{4}$$

To express a percentage as a decimal, we could express it as fraction with a denominator of 100, then as a decimal.   Converting a fraction with a denominator of 100 to a decimal involves simply moving the decimal place over two places to the left. We can do this directly with the percentage.

25% = 0.25

Students also learned in *Primary Mathematics 5B* to convert a 1-place or 2-place decimal to a percentage.   Here the conversion is extended to 3-place decimals. We can think of the decimal as a fraction of 100, and so multiply it by 100%, which simply involves moving the decimal two places to the right.

$0.175 = 0.175 \times 100\% = 17.5\%$

Students will not encounter decimal percentages or fractions which give non-terminating decimals in this unit.

 Learning Tasks 7-11, p. 50

 7.   (a) $5\% = \dfrac{5}{100} = \dfrac{1}{20}$ (b) $8\% = \dfrac{8}{100} = \dfrac{2}{25}$ (c) $50\% = \dfrac{50}{100} = \dfrac{1}{2}$

(d) $15\% = \dfrac{15}{100} = \dfrac{3}{20}$ (e) $44\% = \dfrac{44}{100} = \dfrac{11}{25}$ (f) $78\% = \dfrac{78}{100} = \dfrac{39}{50}$

8.   **80%**

9.   **7.5%**

10. (a) **10%**   (b) **90%**   (c) **1%**   (d) **3%**
    (e) **75%**   (f) **0.1 %**   (g) **4.5%**   (h) **22.5%**

11. (a) **0.03**   (b) **0.35**   (c) **0.4**   (d) **0.86**

 Practice 4A, p. 53, #1-3
Use these problems for additional practice during the lesson, if needed. Answers are on p. 51.

 Workbook Exercise 16

(3) Word Problems (p. 51)

 ➢ Solve word problems involving percentage.

 As your student starts encountering more complicated percentage problems in the next few sections, it will become increasingly important to determine clearly what is to be taken as the whole quantity. Use the simpler problems here to emphasize the quantity that is the whole. In this section it will be the quantity that comes after the word "of".

 Learning Task 12, p. 51
Ask your student what is going to be the whole in this problem. In both (a) and (b) it is the total number of students. Point out the phrase "of the ..."

 12. (a) **70%** walk to school.   (b) **30%** go by bus.

 Practice 4A, p. 53, problems #4-9
Use some or all of these problems for additional problems during this lesson, if necessary. Answers are on pp. 51-52.

In each of the problems, have your student tell you what is to be taken as the whole, and note that the quantity following the phrase "of the..." will be the quantity that is the whole. You can have her draw the whole as a bar and indicate the other information on the diagram for some of the problems. Diagrams are a good way to organize the information and will become more important in later problems. It is not necessary to diagram all the problems if your student is not having any difficulty.

 Workbook Exercise 17

---

(4) Percentage of a Percentage (p. 51)

➤ Solve word problems involving percentage of a percentage.

  Draw a bar and mark 60%.   Tell
your student this is 60% of the total.

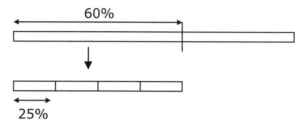

Draw another bar underneath the
same length as the 60% and tell
your student this is now the total.
Ask her to mark 25% of this new
bar.

This is 25% of the 60%. Tell her we need to find out what percentage it is of
the original bar. We can think of the 60% bar as consisting of 60 1% units.

25% of them would be $\frac{25}{100} = \frac{1}{4}$ of them, or $\frac{1}{4} \times 60 = 15$. 15 of the 60 units

is 25% of 60. $\frac{15}{60} = 25\%$. The original bar has 100 1% units of the same size.

So those 15 units are 15% of the original whole bar.

So to find a percentage of a percentage in terms of the original total, we can
multiply the percentage *by* the percentage.

$$25\% \text{ of } 60\% = \frac{25}{100} \times 60\% = 15\%$$

25% of 60% = 15% of 100%

Have your student find some other percentages of a percentage:

$$50\% \text{ of } 50\% = \frac{50}{100} \times 50\% = \frac{50}{\underset{2}{\cancel{100}}} \times \cancel{50}^{1} = 25\%$$

20% of 80% = 16%

30% of 75% = 22.5%

 Learning Task 13, p. 51

  13. (a) 40% + 15% = **55%**   (b) $\frac{45}{100} \times \$120 = \$54$

 Practice 4A, p. 53, problem 10
Use this problem as an additional learning task, if necessary. Answer is on
p. 52.

 Workbook Exercise 18

(5) Percentage Increase and Decrease (p. 52)

 ➤ Solve word problems involving tax, interest, increase, decrease, and discount.

 Students learned how to solve problems involving tax, interest, increase, decrease, and discount in *Primary Mathematics 5B*. This is reviewed here.

Tax, interest, or increase is given as a percentage of the original amount. After we find the numerical amount for the tax, interest or increase, we can add it to the original amount to find the new amount. Decrease and discount is also given as a percentage of the original amount. After we find the numerical amount for the decrease or discount, we can subtract it from the original amount to find the new amount.

 Learning Tasks 14-16, p. 52
Continue to ask your student for the quantity that is to be taken as the whole. You can also call it the *base*.

 14. Whole or base is the normal cost, or $40 + $15.

$$\text{Discount} = \frac{20}{100} \times \$55 = \$11$$

$55 – $11 = **$44**

15. Whole or base is the number of members last year, or 140.

$$\text{Increase} = \frac{15}{100} \times 140 = 21$$

140 + 21 = **161**

16. Whole or base is the cost of the bicycle.

$$\text{Tax} = \frac{3}{100} \times \$600 = \$18$$

$600 + $18 = **$618**

 In these solutions, the actual value of the discount, increase, or tax is found first.

You may want to discuss an alternate approach.

14. Since there is a 20% discount, the new cost of the items is
100% – 20% = of the old cost.

$$\text{Final cost} = \frac{80}{100} \times \$55 = \$44$$

15. If the membership increases by 15%, the new membership is 100% + 15% = 115% of the original membership.

New membership = $\dfrac{115}{100} \times 140 = 161$

16. The new cost is 100% + 3% = 103% of the old cost.

New cost = $\dfrac{103}{100} \times \$600 = \$618$

➤ Ask your student whether, if there is a decrease of 10%, followed by an increase of 10%, the final cost will end up the same as the old cost. Have her work out the answer.

At item costs $100. What is its cost after a 10% decrease?

10% of $100 = $\dfrac{1}{100} \times 100 = 10$

New cost after decrease = $100 – $10 = $90

Now there is a 10% increase. What is the new cost? Note that the 10% increase is a 10% increase of $90, not $100.

10% of $90 = $\dfrac{10}{100} \times 90 = \$9$

New cost after increase = $90 + $9 = $99

The final cost is not the same as the initial cost, because the base, or whole, changes. The decrease is a percentage of the original amount, but the increase is a percentage of the amount after the decrease.

 Workbook Exercise 19

> **Practice (pp. 53-54)**

 ➢ Practice solving percentage problems.

 Practice 4A, p. 53

 1. (a) $8\% = \dfrac{8}{100} = \dfrac{2}{25}$ (b) $25\% = \dfrac{25}{100} = \dfrac{1}{4}$

   (c) $50\% = \dfrac{50}{100} = \dfrac{1}{2}$ (d) $66\% = \dfrac{66}{100} = \dfrac{33}{50}$

2. (a) **0.09**   (b) **0.9**   (c) **0.15**   (d) **0.62**

3. (a) $\dfrac{2}{5} \times 100\% = \mathbf{40\%}$ (b) $\dfrac{7}{8} \times 100\% = \mathbf{87.5\%}$

   (c) $\dfrac{9}{20} \times 100\% = \mathbf{45\%}$ (d) $\dfrac{30}{600} \times 100\% = \mathbf{5\%}$

   (e) $0.5 \times 100\% = \mathbf{50\%}$ (f) $0.08 \times 100\% = \mathbf{8\%}$

   (g) $0.15 \times 100\% = \mathbf{15\%}$ (h) $0.245 \times 100\% = \mathbf{24.5\%}$

4. "of her pocket money" – the whole is her pocket money.

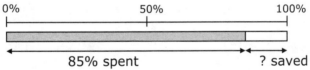

Percentage of her pocket money saved = $100\% - 85\% = \mathbf{15\%}$

5. "of a pole" – the length of the pole is the whole.
   Percentage of the pole painted white = $100\% - 45\% - 20\% = \mathbf{35\%}$

6. "of the seats" – the 400 seats is the whole.
   Percentage vacant = $\dfrac{36}{400} \times 100\% = \mathbf{9\%}$

7. **US›** "of the students" – total students is the whole.
   3d› "of the pupils" – total pupils is the whole.

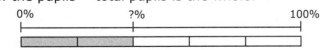

Percentage of the students that wear glasses = $\dfrac{2}{5} \times 100\% = \mathbf{40\%}$

8. whole = total length of cloth
    3 m = 300 cm

    Percentage of cloth used for dress = $\dfrac{75}{300} \times 100\% =$ **25%**

9. whole = total medals
    Number of gold medals = 45 − 22 − 14 = 9

    Percentage of total that were gold medals = $\dfrac{9}{45} \times 100\% =$ **20%**

10.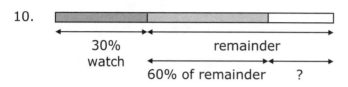

    Savings left is 40% of remainder. Remainder is 70% of total.

    40% of 70% = $\dfrac{40}{100} \times 70\% = 28\%$

    She has **28%** of her savings left.

 Practice 4B, p. 54

 1. (a) $\dfrac{9}{100} \times 125 =$ **11.25**   (b) $\dfrac{78}{100} \times 900 =$ **702**

       (c) $\dfrac{30}{100} \times \$250 =$ **$75**   (d) $\dfrac{45}{100} \times 400 \text{ m} =$ **180 m**

       (e) $\dfrac{21}{100} \times 50 \text{ } \ell =$ **10.5 ℓ**   (f) $\dfrac{16}{100} \times 60 \text{ kg} =$ **9.6 kg**

2. Interest = 4% of $1500 = $\dfrac{4}{100} \times \$1500 =$ **$60**

3. Percentage that did not hit the target = 100% − 40% = 60%
    Number of arrows that did not hit = 60% of 15 = $\dfrac{60}{100} \times 15 =$ **9**

4. Percentage not air-conditioned = 100% − 64% = 36%
    Number of rooms not air-conditioned = 36% of 125 = $\dfrac{36}{100} \times 125 =$ **45**

5. Discount = 5% of $200 = $\dfrac{1}{2}$ of 10% of $200 = $\dfrac{1}{2}$ of $20 = $10
    Selling price = $200 − $10 = **$190**

6. Increase = 5% of $1400 = $\dfrac{1}{2}$ of 10% of $1400 = $\dfrac{1}{2}$ of $140 = $70
    New salary = $1400 + $70 = **$1470**

7. Percentage of the total which are European stamps
    = 100% – 60% – 24% = 16%

    Number of European stamps = 16% of 300 = $\frac{16}{100} \times 300$ = **48**

8.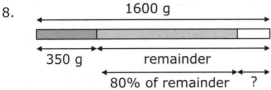

    Remainder = 1600 – 350 = 1250
    She had 20% of the remainder left.

    20% of 1250 g = $\frac{1}{5} \times 1250$ g = 250 g

    She had **250 g** left.

9.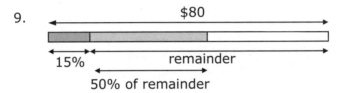

    Remainder is 100% – 15% = 85%

    85% of $80 = $\frac{85}{100} \times \$80$ = $68

    50% of that, or $\frac{1}{2}$, is spent on meat.

    Amount spent on meat = $\frac{1}{2} \times \$68$ = **$34**

10. Number of girls = 60% of 40 = $\frac{6}{10} \times 40$ = 24

    Number of boys = 40 – 24 = 16

    Number of girls that wear glasses = 50% of 24 = $\frac{1}{2} \times 24$ = 12

    Number of boys who wear glasses = 25% of 16 = $\frac{1}{4} \times 16$ = 4

    Total number of students who wear glasses = 12 + 4 = **16**

Part 2 – One Quantity as a Percentage of Another

(1) One Quantity as a Percentage of Another (pp. 55-57)

> ➢ Express one quantity as a percentage of another.

To express a quantity as a percentage of another, the second quantity is taken as 100%. It is the base. If the first quantity is smaller than the second quantity, the percentage is smaller than 100%. If the first quantity is greater than the second quantity, the percentage is greater than 100%. Two methods may be used to solve these problems. For example:

Express $500 as a percentage of $400 (p. 55 in the text).

Here, $400 is the base. Note the use of the word "of" before $400 as a key to finding the quantity that is to be taken as the base.

Method 1:
Take $400 as 100%.
$400 $\longrightarrow$ 100%

$1 $\longrightarrow \dfrac{100}{400}\% = \dfrac{1}{4}\%$

$500 $\longrightarrow \dfrac{1}{4}\% \times 500 = 125\%$

Method 2:
Write $500 as a fraction of $400 and then write the fraction as a percentage.

$\dfrac{500}{400} \times 100\% = \dfrac{5}{4} \times 100\%$

$= 5 \times 25\%$

$= 125\%$

Express $400 as a percentage of $500 (p. 56 in the text).

Method 1:
Take $500 as 100%.
$500 $\longrightarrow$ 100%

$1 $\longrightarrow \dfrac{100}{500}\% = \dfrac{1}{5}\%$

$400 $\longrightarrow \dfrac{1}{5}\% \times 400 = 80\%$

Method 2:
Write $400 as a fraction of $500 and then write the fraction as a percentage.

$\dfrac{400}{500} \times 100\% = \dfrac{4}{5} \times 100\%$

$= 4 \times 20\%$

$= 80\%$

Allow your student to use either method. The second method is more common and is used in most of the examples in the text, though the first method is used on pp. 55-56 and shows a unitary approach similar to what was used with rates in Primary Mathematics 5B. Once we know what 1% of the total $1 is, we can find the percentage of any dollar amount.

When finding one quantity as a percentage of another, both quantities must be expressed in the same unit of measurement. To avoid decimals, we convert the amount that represents the larger measurement unit into the smaller measurement unit. So if we want to find what percent 50¢ is of $2, we convert the $2 into cents first, and find 50¢ as a percentage of 200¢.

Page 55

Have your student tell you the quantity that is to be taken as 100%, or the base. Since we are finding Meihua's savings as a percentage **of** Sumin's savings, Sumin's savings is the base. Point out that the base is often the quantity following the word "of" in these types of problems.

Tell your student we can solve this by first finding how much $1 is as a percentage of Sumin's savings. Once we find that, we can find any quantity in dollars as a percentage of Sumin's savings.

To express $1 as a percentage of the $400, we can first find it as a fraction of the total.

$$\frac{1}{400} = \frac{1}{400} \times 100\% = \frac{100}{400}\%$$

Or, we can imagine Sumin's bar as divided up into 400 units and the percentage ruler is divide up into 100 units. 1 unit on the bar is what value on the percentage ruler? Or, if the total is 100%, and there are 400 equal parts, how many % is in one part? A $1 unit is $\frac{100}{400}\% = \frac{1}{4}\%$ of 400 units.

If your student has trouble with this, use a simpler example, first where the amount in a part will be a whole number, and then where it will be a fraction. For example:

If the total is 10, and we have two equal parts, how do we find the number in each part. We divide: $10 \div 2 = 5$; there are 5 in each part.

If the total is 10 and we have 10 equal parts, how many are in each part.

     $10 \div 10 = 1$. There is 1 in each part.

If the total is 10 and we have 20 equal parts, how many are in each part?

     $10 \div 20 = \frac{10}{20} = \frac{1}{2}$

If the total is 10 and we have 40 equal parts, how many are in each part?

     $10 \div 40 = \frac{10}{40} = \frac{1}{4}$

If the total is 100, and we have 400 equal parts, how many are in each part?

     $100 \div 400 = \frac{100}{400} = \frac{1}{4}$

You can also show your student a meter stick. There are 100 centimeters. If we wanted to cut the meter stick up into 400 equal sections, how long would each section be?

Now that we know what percentage of Sumin's savings is $1, we can find what percentage of Sumin's savings for any other dollar amount.

If $1 is $\frac{1}{4}$%, or $\frac{100}{400}$% of $400, then $500 is $500 times more, or $\frac{100}{400}$% × $500.

Point out that we can simplify $\frac{100}{400}$ × 500 different ways and get the same answer.

$$\frac{100}{400} \times 500 = \frac{1}{\cancel{4}_1} \times \cancel{500}^{125} = 125 \qquad \frac{100}{400} \times 500 = \frac{\cancel{100}^{25}}{\cancel{400}_1} \times \cancel{500}^5 = 125$$

The answer is greater than 100% because Meihua's savings is more than Sumin's saving.

Read the sentence in the gray box "Meihua saves 25% more than Sumin" and ask your student, how would we know what is the base, given just that phrase,. This sentence could be written more explicitly as "Meihua's savings is 25% more than Sumin's savings." The quantity after the word **than** is the base. The sentence could be written even more explicitly as "Meihua's savings is 25% of Sumin's savings more than Sumin's savings."

Discuss the second method with this problem.

We can find Meihua's savings as a fraction of Sumin's savings and then convert to a percentage. We first find $500 as a fraction of $400. $400 is the total, and goes in the denominator.

$$500 \text{ is } \frac{500}{400} \text{ of } 400 \text{ or } \frac{5}{4} \text{ of } 400.$$

Then we multiply by 100% to express the fraction as a percentage.

$$\frac{500}{400} \times 100\% = 125\%$$

Point out that 125% is $\frac{5}{4}$. $125\% = \frac{125}{100} = \frac{5}{4}$. Meihua's savings is $\frac{5}{4}$ of Sumin's savings. Meihua's savings is 125% of Sumin's savings.

Page 56

Discuss the method shown. The total is 100%, and there are 500 equal parts, so there are $\frac{100}{500}$% in each part. $1 is $\frac{100}{500}$% (or $\frac{1}{5}$%) of Meihua's savings. So $400 is $400 times the percentage for $1.

Also discuss the method where we first find what fraction Sumin's savings is of Meihua's savings, and then find the percentage. The base is now $500.

$$\frac{400}{500} \times 100\% = 80\%$$

Point out that 80% is $\frac{4}{5}$. $80\% = \frac{80}{100} = \frac{4}{5}$. Sumin's savings is $\frac{4}{5}$ of Meihua's savings. Sumin's savings is 80% of Meihua's savings.

Read the sentence in the gray box "Sumin saves 20% less than Meihua" and ask your student how we would know what is the base, given just that phrase. This sentence could be written more explicitly as "Sumin's savings is 20% less than Meihua's savings." The quantity after the word **than** is the base.

Note the thought bubble at the bottom of the page. Ask your student why the two percentages are different, even though Meihua's savings and Sumin's savings is the same in both. They are different because the quantity for 100% is different. If the first quantity is 25% more than the second, it does not follow that the second quantity is 25% less than the first. This is an important point to make.

 Learning Tasks 1-3, p. 57

Make sure your student understands that to find one measurement as a percentage of another measurement, both measurements have to be in the same measuring unit. We usually change the quantity with the larger unit of measurement into a value with the smaller unit of measurement (e.g. dollars to cents or liters to milliliters).

In each of these learning tasks, have your student tell you what the base is and how she knows.

 1. **10**%   2. **15**%   3. **150**%

Practice 4C, p. 60, #1-4
Use these problems if your student needs more learning tasks for discussion.
Answers are on p. 61.

 US›

Ask your student to find one measurement as a percentage of another using US measurement. Avoid answers that are repeating decimals.

- What percentage of 5 feet is 6 inches?
  5 feet = 60 inches.
  $\frac{6}{60} \times 100\% = 10\%$. Or, since 6 inches is half a foot, imagine the 5 feet divided into half-foot units. There would be 10 units, and one unit is 10%.

- What percentage of 5 feet is 9 inches?
  $\frac{9}{60} \times 100\% = 15\%$.

- Express 1 quart as a percentage of 1 gallon.
  $\frac{1}{4} \times 100\% = 25\%$

- Express 1 ounce as a percentage of 1 pound.
  $\frac{1}{16} \times 100\% = 6.25\%$

 Workbook Exercise 20

---

(2) Word Problems I (pp. 57-58)

- ➤ Solve word problems involving one quantity as a percentage of another.
- ➤ Find percent increase or decrease.
- ➤ Relate selling price to cost price as a percentage.

 In the last section, students were given the increase, decrease, or discount as a percentage of a quantity, such as the cost of an item, and asked to find the new cost. In this section, they are given the old and new price, and asked to find the new price as a percentage of the old price, or to find the increase, decrease, or discount as a percentage of the old price.

Learning Tasks 4-6 pp. 57-59

 4. Ask your student for the base or the quantity to be taken as 100% (the cost price). Note that the base is the quantity in the denominator. **75**%

5. (b) The base is the usual price.   **20**%

6. The base is her weight last year. **7.5**%

 Practice 4C, p. 60, #5-8
Use these problems if your student needs more learning tasks for discussion. Answers are on p. 61.

 Workbook Exercise 21

---

(3) Word Problems II (pp. 58-59)

 ➢ Find percent more or less one quantity is than another.
➢ Find a quantity given the percent more or less.

 To find how many percent one quantity is more or less than another, first find the difference between the two quantities and then express the difference as a percentage of the smaller or larger quantity.

In problems that involve a percentage as more or less *than* a quantity, the base can be found using the word "than." The quantity that comes after the word "than" is the quantity that we are comparing another quantity *to*, so it is the base.

 Learning Tasks 7-9, pp. 58-79

7. Lead your student to see that in order to find how many percent more men than women there are, we need to first find how many more men *than* women there are. Make sure your student knows what quantity is to be taken as the base. It is the number of women. The number *more* men is being compared to the number *of* women.

 Difference in number = 50 – 40 = **10**

Method 1: Take the number of women as 100%.
$40 \longrightarrow 100\%$
$10 \longrightarrow \dfrac{100}{40}\% \times 10 = \textbf{25\%}$

Method 2: Express 10 as a fraction of 40 and then write the fraction as a percentage.
$\dfrac{10}{40} \times 100\% = 25\%$

US› 8.   Since Brandon's money is being compared to Ian's money (he has 20% more *than* Ian) take Ian's money as 100%.   The 100% is one whole amount of money, which is $56.   Brandon has 20% more *than* Ian, so he has 100% + 20% = 120% *of* Ian's money

120% of $56 = $\dfrac{120}{100} \times \$56 = \$\mathbf{67.20}$

3d› 8.   Since Rahmat's money is being compared to Ali's money (he has 20% more *than* Ali) take Ali's money as 100%.   The 100% is one whole amount of money, which is $56.   Rahmat has 20% more *than* Ali, so he has 100% + 20% = 120% *of* Ali's money

120% of $56 = $\dfrac{120}{100} \times \$56 = \$\mathbf{67.20}$

9.   The weight of Package B is being compared to the weight of Package A, so take the weight of Package A as 100%.   Package B weighs 15% less *than* Package A, so the weight of Package B is 100% − 15% = 85% of the weight *of* Package A.

85% of 5 kg = $\dfrac{85}{100} \times 5$ kg = **4.25** kg.

Practice 4C, p. 60, #9-10
Use these problems if your student needs more learning tasks for discussion. Answers are on p. 61.

Workbook Exercises 22-23

Practice (p. 60)

 ➤ Solve problems involving one quantity as a percentage of another.

 Practice 4C, p. 60

1. 1.5 ℓ = 1,500 ml

$$\frac{480}{1500} \times 100 = \mathbf{32\%}$$

2. 2 h = 120 min

$$\frac{30}{120} \times 100 = \mathbf{25\%}$$

3. (a) $\frac{36}{24} \times 100\% = \mathbf{150\%}$ (b) $\frac{36-24}{24} \times 100\% = \frac{12}{24} \times 100\%$

$$= \mathbf{50\%}$$

4. 2.5 kg = 2,500 g

$$\frac{650}{2500} \times 100\% = 26\%$$

26% of the sugar was used for making syrup.

5. Percentage reduction $= \dfrac{200-150}{200} \times 100\% = \dfrac{50}{200} \times 100\% = \mathbf{25\%}$

6. Percentage increase $= \dfrac{96-80}{80} \times 100\% = \dfrac{16}{80} \times 100\% = \mathbf{20\%}$

7. Percentage increase $= \dfrac{15-12}{12} \times 100\% = \dfrac{3}{12} \times 100\% = \mathbf{25\%}$

8. Percentage discount $= \dfrac{60-51}{60} \times 100\% = \dfrac{9}{60} \times 100\% = \mathbf{15\%}$

9. Number of women = 600 – 250 = 350

    Percent more women $= \dfrac{350-250}{250} \times 100\% = \dfrac{100}{250} \times 100\% = \mathbf{40\%}$

10. Amount Nancy saved = $35 – $10 = $25

    Percent more Mary saved than Nancy $= \dfrac{10}{25} \times 100\% = \mathbf{40\%}$

Part 3 – Solving Percentage Problems by Unitary Method

(1) Percentage Problems I (p. 62)

➢ Find the whole given the value of a percentage part.

In these problems students are given the value of a percentage part and asked to find the whole. For example, if 75% of the whole is 12, what is the whole? Or, rephrased, 12 is 75% of what? Students find the answer using a unitary method where they first find the value of 1%.

75% of the whole is 12

1% of the whole is $\dfrac{12}{75}$

100% of the whole is $\dfrac{12}{75} \times 100 = 16$

Students have already done something similar to this with fractions. In Primary Mathematics 4A, they learned to solve problems such as the following:

Mary spent $\dfrac{3}{4}$ of her money on a book that cost $12. How much money did she start with?

To solve this, students drew a bar diagram, showing fourths as units, labeled 3 of them as $12, found the value for 1 of the units, and then multiplied by 4 to find the value for all 4 units.

3 units, or $\dfrac{3}{4}$ ⟶ $12

1 unit, or $\dfrac{1}{4}$ ⟶ $\dfrac{12}{4}$

4 units, or $\dfrac{4}{4}$ ⟶ $\dfrac{12}{4} \times 4 = 16$

The arrow can be read "of the whole is" which in this case is "of her total money is".

The unitary method for solving percentage problems is very similar, except that there are 100 units on the whole bar.

75 units or 75% ⟶ 12

1 unit, or 1% ⟶ $\dfrac{12}{75}$

100 units, or 100% ⟶ $\dfrac{12}{75} \times 100 = 16$

Once we find the value for 1%, we can find the value for any other percentage part of the whole. If we are given that 75% of the total is 12, and need to find 20% of the total, we can first find the value for 1%, and then multiply that by 20 to find the quantity for 20% of the total.

All the examples in the text have the student finding the value for 1%. Your student may be able to use shortcuts to simplify the problem. In the above example, she might recognize 75% as being $\frac{3}{4}$, and find $\frac{1}{4}$, or 25% first.

$$\div 3 \left(\begin{array}{l} 75\% \longrightarrow 12 \\ 25\% \longrightarrow \frac{12}{3} = 4 \end{array} \right. \hspace{1cm} \left. \begin{array}{l} \\ \\ \end{array} \right) \div 3$$
$$\times 4 \left(\begin{array}{l} \\ 100\% \longrightarrow 4 \times 4 = 16 \end{array} \right. \hspace{1cm} \left. \begin{array}{l} \\ \end{array} \right) \times 4$$

As with any of the learning tasks, you can present the problem to your student without letting him or her see the solution. Let your student try to work out a solution and then discuss it with you. Then compare his approach to the text's approach.

Save the example on p. 61 until after learning task 3 on p. 63.

 Learning Task 1, p. 62

Tell your student to imagine the bar as being divided up into 100 equal parts. Each part is $\frac{1}{100}$ of the total, or 1% of the total.

We are told how much 75 units, or 75% of the total, is. We need to find the total.

If 75 units, or 75% of the total, is 42, how do we find what one unit is? We can divide 42 by 75. This is what is shown in the first two lines of the solution. The arrow can be read as "of the total is". We can think of the first two lines are similar to

$$75 \text{ units} = 42$$
$$1 \text{ unit} = \frac{42}{75}$$

We don't need to solve this fraction right away. (If we did, we would find out that 1 unit = \$0.56.)

Now that we know what 1 unit, or 1% is, how do we find what 100 units, or 100% is? We multiply by 100. The next line is similar to

$$100 \text{ units} = \frac{42}{75} \times 100$$

We can solve this problem by simplifying first.

$$\frac{42}{75} \times 100 = \frac{42}{75_3} \times 100^4 = \frac{42^{14}}{75_{3_1}} \times 100^4 = 14 \times 4 = 56$$

☑ The total score was **56**.

Point out to your student that we do the same thing to the numbers on both side of the arrow in order to maintain their proportion to each other.

$$\div 75 \left(\begin{array}{l} 75\% \longrightarrow 42 \\ \qquad 1\% \longrightarrow \dfrac{42}{75} \end{array} \right.$$

$$\times 100 \left(\begin{array}{l} \\ 100\% \longrightarrow \dfrac{42}{75} \times 100 \end{array} \right.$$

$$\left. \begin{array}{l} \\ \\ \end{array} \right\rangle \div 75$$

$$\left. \begin{array}{l} \\ \\ \end{array} \right\rangle \times 100$$

$$75 : 42 = 1 : ?$$

$$1 : \dfrac{42}{75} = 100 : ?$$

 Learning Task 2, p. 24

Discuss this problem with your student. Make sure he understands why (**US**› Adam's, **3d**› Rahim's) salary is the base. Jim's salary is five as a percentage *of* (**US**› Adam's, **3d**› Rahim's) salary. So it is being compared to (**US**› Adam's, **3d**› Rahim's) salary.

 (**US**› Adam's, **3d**› Rahim's) salary is $**960**.

 Practice 4D, p. 67, problems 1-4
You can use these problems for additional learning tasks, if necessary. Answers are on p. 68.

 Workbook Exercise 24

---

(2) Percentage Problems II (pp. 63-64, p. 61)

➢ Find the original value given the new value and the percent increase or decrease.
➢ Find the new value given the value of the percent increase or decrease.

 Learning Task 3, p. 63

Make sure your student knows what quantity is the base. We are given the percent price reduction *of the usual price*, so the usual price is the base. Knowing the value for 85%, which is the selling price of $17, we can find the value for 100%.

The usual price of the blouse is $**20**.

 **Page 61**

The increase in the selling price is being compared to the cost price. So the cost price is the base. Since he is selling the furniture for more than it cost, the selling price is going to be more than 100% of the cost price. Here, the student can imagine the cost price bar having 100 units. The selling price bar has 120 units. If we know the value for 120 units, we can find the value for 1 unit (1%) and then the value for 100 units (100%, which is the cost price.

☑ The cost price of the set of furniture is **$3000**.

You may want to point out to your student that we do not always have to go down to 1%. When the percent for which we are given the value is a multiple of 10, it is just as easy to find the value for 10%.

$$\div 12 \left(\begin{array}{l} 120\% \longrightarrow \$3600 \\ 10\% \longrightarrow \dfrac{3600}{12} \\ 100\% \longrightarrow \dfrac{3600}{12} \times 10 \end{array} \right) \begin{array}{l} \div 12 \\ \\ \times 10 \end{array}$$

If your student uses this approach, she needs to be careful to keep track of what she is doing and not multiply by 100 at the end just because she might usually do that. Make sure your student takes the time to determine if an answer makes sense. If she first divides by 12 and then multiplies by 100 instead by mistake, the answer will be $30,000 instead, which doesn't make sense — for one thing, the cost price can't be more than the selling price if there was an increase.

 Learning Tasks 4-6, pp. 63-64

 4. We are given the percent increase of the original number of books, so the original number is the base.
    There were **150** books in the library before the increase.

5. We are given the percentage increase, so the base is her monthly salary before the increase. We are given a value for 10% of this salary and can find the value for the salary either before the increase (100%) or after the increase (110%).
    10% of her original monthly salary is $120.

Since the percentage of the new salary is an easy multiple of the percentage value we are given, it is not necessary to determine the value for 1%.	Or:
10% ⟶ $120 110% ⟶ $120 × 11 = $1320	10% ⟶ $120 1% ⟶ $$\dfrac{120}{10}$$ 110% ⟶ $$\$\dfrac{120}{10} \times 110 = \$1320$$

    Her monthly salary after the increase is **$1320**.

6. The base is the cost price. We are given a value for 80% of the cost price.
    We can find the cost price, and then add $150 to that to find the price he
    must sell at to make $150 above the cost price.
    80% of the cost price is $600.

    $$80\% \longrightarrow \$600$$

    $$1\% \longrightarrow \$\frac{600}{80}$$

    $$100\% \longrightarrow \$\frac{600}{80} \times 100 = \$750$$

    The cost price is $750. To make $150, the selling price must be
    $750 + $150 = **$900**

 Practice 4D, p. 67, problems 5-8
You can use these problems for additional learning tasks, if necessary.
Answers are on p. 69.

 Workbook Exercise 25

---

(3) Percentage Problems III (pp. 65-66)

 ➢ Solve problems involving percentage using the unitary method.

 Learning Tasks 7-10, pp. 65-66
Make sure in each task that your student understands what value is to be taken
as the base.

 7. He saved 10% more in June *than in May*. The percentage increase is being
    compared to the amount saved in May, so the base is the savings in May.
    110% of the savings in May is $44.

    $$110\% \longrightarrow \$44$$

    $$1\% \longrightarrow \$\frac{44}{110}$$

    $$100\% \longrightarrow \$\frac{44}{110} \times 100 = \$40$$

    He saved **$40** in May.

8. She has 10% fewer books *than John*. We are given the difference as a percentage of John's books so the base is the number of John's books. 90% of John's books is 180.

$$90\% \longrightarrow 180$$

$$1\% \longrightarrow \frac{180}{90}$$

$$100\% \longrightarrow \frac{180}{90} \times 100 = 200$$

John has **200** books.

9. We are given the percentage *of total teachers* that are male, so the total number of teachers is the base. If 40% are males, then 60% are females. The difference in percentage is 20%. The difference in number of teachers is 18. So 20% *of the total teachers* is 18. It is *not* correct to say there are 20% more female teachers *than male teachers*. If we did, that would make the base the male teachers. 20% of the total number of teachers is 18.

$$20\% \longrightarrow 18$$

$$1\% \longrightarrow \frac{18}{20}$$

$$100\% \longrightarrow \frac{18}{20} \times 100 = 90$$

There are **90** teachers altogether.

10. We are given a percentage of the spaces, so the total number of spaces is the base. 12% of the total number of spaces is 24.

$$12\% \longrightarrow 24$$

$$1\% \longrightarrow \frac{24}{12}$$

$$8\% \longrightarrow \frac{24}{12} \times 8 = 16$$

There are **16** spaces for buses.

Practice 4D, p. 67, problems 9-10
You can use these problems for additional learning tasks, if necessary.
Answers are on p. 70.

  Workbook Exercise 26

Practice (pp. 67-68)

 ➤ Solve problems involving percentage.

 Practice 4D, p. 67

  1. The base is her monthly salary. 20% of her monthly salary is $240.
$$20\% \longrightarrow \$240$$
$$1\% \longrightarrow \$\frac{240}{20}$$
$$100\% \longrightarrow \$\frac{240}{20} \times 100 = \$1200$$
Her monthly salary is **$1200**.

2. The base is the number of entries. 12% of the entries is 132.
$$12\% \longrightarrow 132$$
$$1\% \longrightarrow \frac{132}{12}$$
$$100\% \longrightarrow \frac{132}{12} \times 100 = 1100$$
There were **1100** entries.

3. The base is the total number of questions.
Percentage of the questions he answered incorrectly = 100% – 90% = 10%
10% of the questions is 5.
$$10\% \longrightarrow 5$$
$$90\% \longrightarrow 5 \times 9 = 45$$
He answered **45** questions correctly.

4. The base is the number of books in the library.
Percentage of books for children = 100% – 60% – 5% = 35%
35% of the books is 280.
$$35\% \longrightarrow 280$$
$$1\% \longrightarrow \frac{280}{35}$$
$$100\% \longrightarrow \frac{280}{35} \times 100 = 800$$
There are **800** books.

5. The base is the usual price. 70% of the usual price is $140.
$$70\% \longrightarrow \$140$$
$$1\% \longrightarrow \$\frac{140}{70}$$
$$100\% \longrightarrow \$\frac{140}{70} \times 100 = \$200$$
The usual price of the fan is **$200**.

6. The base is the usual price. 25% of the usual price of the dress is $15.

    $$25\% \longrightarrow \$15$$

    $$1\% \longrightarrow \$\frac{15}{25}$$

    $$100\% \longrightarrow \$\frac{15}{25} \times 100 = \$60$$

    The usual price of the dress is **$60**.

7. The base is the usual price.
    Selling price = 100% − 15% = 85% of the usual price.

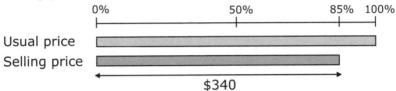

    85% of the usual price is $340.

    $$85\% \longrightarrow \$340$$

    $$1\% \longrightarrow \$\frac{340}{85}$$

    $$100\% \longrightarrow \$\frac{340}{85} \times 100 = \$400$$

    The usual price of the bicycle is **$400**.

8. The score for the English test is the base.
    Math score = 100% + 5% = 105% of the English test score

    0%   50%   100%
                                                          105%
    English score
    Math score
                            84

    105% of the English test score is 84.

    $$105\% \longrightarrow 84$$

    $$1\% \longrightarrow \frac{84}{105}$$

    $$100\% \longrightarrow \frac{84}{105} \times 100 = 80$$

    Her English test score was **80** points.

9. The amount spent last week is the base.
   Amount spent this week = 100% + 10% = 110% of the amount spent last week.

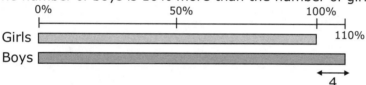

110% of the amount spent last week is $55.

$$110\% \longrightarrow \$55$$

$$1\% \longrightarrow \$\frac{55}{110}$$

$$100\% \longrightarrow \$\frac{55}{110} \times 100 = \$50$$

He spent **$50** last week.

10. The number of girls is the base.
    The number of boys is 10% more than the number of girls.

The total number of children = 100% + 110% = 210% of the number of girls. 10% of the number of girls is 4.

$$10\% \longrightarrow 4$$

$$1\% \longrightarrow \frac{4}{10}$$

$$210\% \longrightarrow \frac{4}{10} \times 210 = 84$$

There are **84** children.

  Practice 4E, p. 68

1. 1.5 kg = 1,500 g

   Percentage = $\frac{600}{1500} \times 100\% = \mathbf{40\%}$

2. 40% of the students are girls.

   $$40\% \longrightarrow 16$$

   $$1\% \longrightarrow \frac{16}{40}$$

   $$60\% \longrightarrow \frac{16}{40} \times 60 = 24$$

   There are **24** boys in the class.

3. His pay is 100% – 20% = 80% of his supervisor's pay
   80% of his supervisor's pay is $1500.

   $$80\% \longrightarrow \$1500$$

   $$1\% \longrightarrow \frac{1500}{80}$$

   $$100\% \longrightarrow \frac{1500}{80} \times 100 = \$1875$$

   His supervisor's pay is **$1875**.

4. The tire is sold at 100% – 10% = 90% of its usual price.
   90% of the usual price is $45.

   $$90\% \longrightarrow \$45$$

   $$1\% \longrightarrow \frac{45}{90}$$

   $$100\% \longrightarrow \frac{45}{90} \times 100 = \$50$$

   The usual price of the tire is **$50**.

US> 5. (a) The base is the total number of problems.

   Number Tim answered correctly = 80% of 50 = $\frac{80}{100} \times 50 = 40$

   Number Carlos answered correctly = 90% of 50 = $\frac{90}{100} \times 50 = 45$

   45 – 40 = 5
   Carlos answered 45 – 40 = **5** more questions correctly than Tim.

   (b) The base is how many questions Carlos answered correctly. It is NOT the total number of questions. We need to find the difference as a percentage of the 40.

   $$\frac{5}{40} \times 100\% = 12.5\%$$

   Carlos answered **12.5%** more questions correctly than Tim.

3d> 5. (a) The base is the total number of problems.

   Number Ali answered correctly = 80% of 50 = $\frac{80}{100} \times 50 = 40$

   Number Osman answered correctly = 90% of 50 = $\frac{90}{100} \times 50 = 45$

   45 – 40 = 5
   Osman answered 45 – 40 = **5** more questions correctly than Ali.

   (b) The base is how many questions Osman answered correctly. It is *not* the total number of questions. We need to find the difference as a percentage of the 40.

   $$\frac{5}{40} \times 100\% = 12.5\%$$

   Osman answered **12.5%** more questions correctly than Ali.

6. To find how many more percent males than females there are, we need to find the number more males than females, and find that as a percentage of the number of females. So we need to find the number of females, which is the base.

Number of males = 60% of 200 = $\dfrac{60}{100} \times 200 = 120$

Number of females = 200 – 120 = 80

Difference = 120 – 80 = 40

$80 \longrightarrow 100\%$ or: $\dfrac{40}{80} \times 100\% = 50\%$
$40 \longrightarrow 50\%$

There are **50%** more males than females.

7. 40% of the beads are red and 60% are yellow.

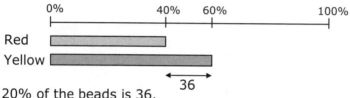

20% of the beads is 36.

$20\% \longrightarrow 36$

$1\% \longrightarrow \dfrac{36}{20}$

$100\% \longrightarrow \dfrac{36}{20} \times 100 = 180$

There are **180** beads.

8. The first customer paid 100% – 20% = 80% of the usual price.

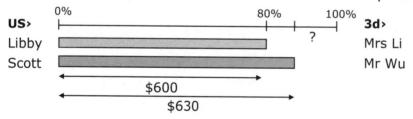

80% of the usual price is $600.

$80\% \longrightarrow \$600$

$1\% \longrightarrow \dfrac{600}{80}$

$100\% \longrightarrow \dfrac{600}{80} \times 100 = \$750$

The usual price is $750.

So the second customer's discount was $750 – $630 = $120

$\dfrac{120}{750} \times 100\% = 16\%$

He was given a **16%** discount.

9. The base is Alice's salary.
    Mary's salary is 110% of Alice's salary.

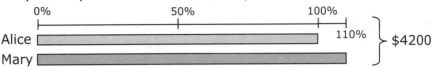

Together they have 100% + 110% = 210% of Alice's salary.
210% of Alice's salary is $4200
$$210\% \longrightarrow \$4200$$
$$1\% \longrightarrow \$\frac{4200}{210}$$
$$110\% \longrightarrow \$\frac{4200}{210} \times 110 = \$2200$$
Mary's salary is **$2200**.

10.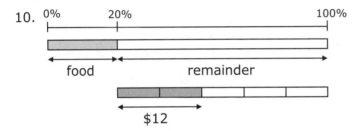

(a) Remainder is 80% of his money.
    $$\frac{2}{5} \text{ of } 80\% = \frac{2}{5} \times 80\% = 32\%$$
    He spent **32%** of his money on the toy.

(b) 32% of his money is $12.
    $$32\% \longrightarrow \$12$$
    $$1\% \longrightarrow \$\frac{12}{32}$$
    $$100\% \longrightarrow \$\frac{12}{32} \times 100 = \$37.50$$
    He had **$37.50** at first.

Review

 Review C, pp. 69-73

 1.   (a) $\dfrac{3}{4}$ (b) $\dfrac{7}{10}$

2. $3 - 2\dfrac{4}{5} = \dfrac{1}{5}$

3.   (a) $\dfrac{3}{8}$ (b) $\dfrac{7}{8}$

      (c) **7**   (d) **2**

4. $\dfrac{3}{5}$

5. $\dfrac{1}{2} \div 6 = \dfrac{1}{2} \times \dfrac{1}{6} = \dfrac{1}{12}$

6.   (a) $\dfrac{7}{20} = \dfrac{35}{100} = \mathbf{0.35}$ (b) $2\dfrac{1}{5} = 2\dfrac{2}{10} = \mathbf{2.2}$

7.   (a) $0.075 = \dfrac{75}{1000} = \dfrac{3}{40}$ (b) $1.04 = 1\dfrac{4}{100} = \mathbf{1\dfrac{1}{25}}$

8. $\dfrac{3}{5}$

9.   **6.96**

10. (a) $\dfrac{20}{120} = \dfrac{1}{6}$ (b) $\dfrac{500}{2000} = \dfrac{1}{4}$

11. (a) $5 \times (\underline{13 - 9}) + \underline{8 \div 4}$ (b) $8 \times (\underline{52 - 47}) \div 2$
        $= \underline{5 \times 4} + 2$ $= \underline{8 \times 5} \div 2$
        $= 20 + 2$ $= \underline{40 \div 2}$
        $= \mathbf{22}$ $= \mathbf{20}$

12. **17.93 km**

13. **0.89**

14. (a) **55,000**   (b) **4**   (c) **4.1**

15. $\dfrac{5}{8} \times 100\% = \mathbf{62.5\%}$

16. **23.5%**

17. (a) $80\% = \dfrac{80}{100} = \dfrac{4}{5}$ (b) $5\% = \dfrac{5}{100} = \dfrac{1}{20}$

18. (a) $6\% = \dfrac{6}{100} = \mathbf{0.06}$ (b) $92\% = \dfrac{92}{100} = \mathbf{0.92}$

19. (a) $\dfrac{5}{100} \times 30 \text{ kg} = \mathbf{1.5 \text{ kg}}$ (b) $\dfrac{60}{100} \times 350 \text{ m} = \mathbf{210 \text{ m}}$

20. $\dfrac{2.5}{10} = \dfrac{25}{100} = \mathbf{25\%}$

21. $\dfrac{2}{5}$ of a number is 42

   $\dfrac{1}{5}$ of a number is $\dfrac{42}{2} = 21$

   $\dfrac{5}{5}$ of a number is $\dfrac{42}{2} \times 5 = 105$

   $\dfrac{1}{3}$ of 105 $= \dfrac{1}{3} \times 105 = \mathbf{35}$

22. Total of the 4 numbers $= 60 \times 4 = 240$
   Total of 3 of the numbers $= 45 + 56 + 75 = 176$
   Fourth number $= 240 - 176 = \mathbf{64}$

23. $\dfrac{1}{2}$ h $\longrightarrow$ 650 revolutions

   1 h $\longrightarrow$ $650 \times 2 = 1300$ revolutions
   3 h $\longrightarrow$ $1300 \times 3 = \mathbf{3900}$ revolutions

24. 5 oranges $\longrightarrow$ \$1.90

   1 orange $\longrightarrow$ \$$\dfrac{1.90}{5}$

   15 oranges $\longrightarrow$ \$$\dfrac{1.90}{5} \times 15 = \mathbf{\$5.70}$

25. \$3 $\longrightarrow$ 5 cans
   \$15 $\longrightarrow$ $5 \times 5 = \mathbf{25}$ cans

26. Find the cost of 6 towels.
   3 towels $\longrightarrow$ \$2.40
   6 towels $\longrightarrow$ $\$2.40 \times 2 = \$4.80$
   Change received $= \$10 - \$4.80 = \mathbf{\$5.20}$

27. 1 unit $= 200 - 50 = 150$
   2 units $= 150 \times 2 = 300$
   There are **300** green balls.

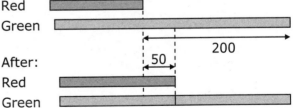

28. Average $= \dfrac{75 + 30}{5} = \dfrac{105}{5} = \mathbf{21\ kg}$

29.   5 oranges $\longrightarrow$ $1.203   3 apples $\longrightarrow$ $1

1 orange $\longrightarrow$ $$\frac{1.20}{5}$$ 1 apple $\longrightarrow$ $$\frac{1}{3}$$

160 oranges $\longrightarrow$ $$\frac{1.20}{5} \times 160$$ 90 apples $\longrightarrow$ $$\frac{1}{3} \times 90$$

= $38.40   = $30

Total money = $38.40 + $30 = **$68.40**

30. $\frac{1}{4}$ of Jim's savings is $350.

$\frac{4}{4}$ of Jim's savings is $350 × 4 = **$1,400**

31.   How many pears could he buy with $\frac{3}{5}$ of his money?

1 mango costs 2 times as much as a pear.
The cost of 1 mango is the cost of 2 pears.
The cost of 15 mangoes is the cost of 15 × 2, or 30 pears.
Buying 15 mangoes and 9 pears would cost the same as buying 30 + 9, or

39 pears. With $\frac{3}{5}$ of his money he can buy 39 pears.

Using this information, how many pears could he buy with the remainder of his money?

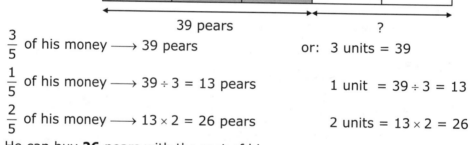

$\frac{3}{5}$ of his money $\longrightarrow$ 39 pears   or: 3 units = 39

$\frac{1}{5}$ of his money $\longrightarrow$ 39 ÷ 3 = 13 pears   1 unit = 39 ÷ 3 = 13

$\frac{2}{5}$ of his money $\longrightarrow$ 13 × 2 = 26 pears   2 units = 13 × 2 = 26

He can buy **26** pears with the rest of his money.

32.   Number of kg he sold at $5.25 = $$\frac{2}{3} \times 18 = 12$$ kg

Amount received = 12 × $5.25 = $63
Remainder = 18 − 12 = 6 kg
Amount received for remainder = 6 × $4.80 = $28.80
Total received = $63 + $28.80 = **$91.80**

33. $\frac{3}{5}$ full is 420 ml

$\frac{1}{5}$ full is $$\frac{420}{3}$$ ml

$\frac{5}{5}$ full is $$\frac{420}{3} \times 5 = 700$$ ml

The capacity of the bottle is **700 ml**.

34.

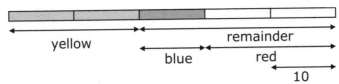

Fraction of blue marbles $= \dfrac{1}{3} \times \dfrac{3}{5} = \dfrac{1}{5}$

Fraction of red marbles $= \dfrac{2}{3} \times \dfrac{3}{5} = \dfrac{2}{5}$

Difference $= \dfrac{2}{5} - \dfrac{1}{5} = \dfrac{1}{5}$

$\dfrac{1}{5}$ of the marbles is 10.   or: 1 unit = 10

$\dfrac{5}{5}$ of the marbles $= 10 \times 5 = 50$ 5 units $= 10 \times 5 = 50$

There are **50** marbles.

35.

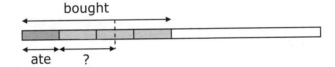

Remainder $= \dfrac{3}{4}$ of $\dfrac{1}{2}$ of cake $= \dfrac{3}{8}$ of cake

Each piece $= \dfrac{1}{2}$ of remainder

$= \dfrac{1}{2}$ of $\dfrac{3}{8}$ of cake $= \dfrac{1}{2} \times \dfrac{3}{8}$ of cake $= \dfrac{3}{16}$ of cake

36.

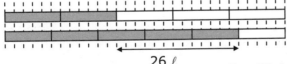

26 ℓ

Or: Divide tank into $5 \times 6 = 30$ units

$\dfrac{5}{6} - \dfrac{2}{5} = \dfrac{25}{30} - \dfrac{12}{30} = \dfrac{13}{30}$ $(5 \times 5) - (2 \times 6)$ units = 13 units

$\dfrac{13}{30} \longrightarrow 26\ \ell.$ 13 units = 26 ℓ

$\dfrac{1}{30} \longrightarrow \dfrac{26}{13}\ \ell = 2\ \ell$ 1 unit $= \dfrac{26}{13}\ \ell = 2\ \ell$

$\dfrac{30}{30} \longrightarrow 2 \times 30 = 60\ \ell$ 30 units $= 2 \times 30 = 60\ \ell$

The capacity of the tank is **60 ℓ**.

37. Number of red balloons = 24 − 6 − 10 = 8
    blue : green : red = 6 : 10 : 8 = **3 : 5 : 4**

38. apples : oranges : pears
       1 :   3
    = 2 :   6

       2   : 9
       2 : 6 : 9

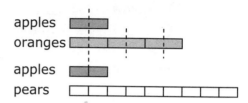

    Total units = 2 + 6 + 9 = 17

    $$\frac{\text{Number of pears}}{\text{Total number of fruit}} = \frac{\mathbf{9}}{\mathbf{17}}$$

39. Discount = 15% of $60 = $\dfrac{15}{100} \times \$60 =$ **$9**

40. Percentage of the members who are boys = 100% − 15% = 85%
    15% of the members is 18
    15% → 18
      1% → $\dfrac{18}{15}$
    85% → $\dfrac{18}{15} \times 85 = 102$
    There are **102** members.

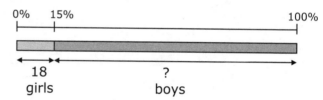

41. Percent of visitors that were adults = 100% − 65% = 35%
    Difference in percent of visitors that were children and percent of visitors
    that were adults = 65% − 35% = 30%
    30% of 480 = $\dfrac{30}{100} \times 480 =$ **144**

42. Henry paid 80% of cost.
    20% of cost = $0.90
    20% ⟶ $0.90
      1% ⟶ $$\dfrac{0.90}{20}$
    80% ⟶ $$\dfrac{0.90}{20} \times 80 =$ **$3.60**

43. Amount of increase = 2000 − 1600 = 400
    Percent increase = $\dfrac{400}{1600} \times 100\% =$ **25%**

44. 120% of the money collected by the games stall is $1,500

    120% $\longrightarrow$ $1500

      1% $\longrightarrow$ $$\dfrac{1500}{120}$$

    100% $\longrightarrow$ $$\dfrac{1500}{120}$ = 1250

The games stall collected **$1250**.

45. Percent of postcards that were foreign = 100% – 20% = 80%

Percent of postcards that were from (**US**› England, **3d**› Malaysia)

= 20% of 80% = $\dfrac{1}{5}$ × 80% = **16%**

46. Base of first triangle = 13 cm – 5cm = 8 cm

Height of first triangle = 2 cm

Area of first triangle = $\dfrac{1}{2}$ × 8 × 2 = 8 cm^2

Base of second triangle = 2 cm (left side is taken as the base)

Height of second triangle = 5 cm

Area of second triangle = $\dfrac{1}{2}$ × 2 × 5 = 5 cm^2

Total area = 8 cm^2 + 5 cm^2 = **13 cm^2**

47. Shaded area = area of square – area of triangle

$$= (10 \times 10) - (\dfrac{1}{2} \times 8 \times 10)$$

$$= 100 - 40$$

$$= \textbf{60 cm}^2$$

48. **C**

49. (a) Average $= \dfrac{15 + 28 + 17 + 12 + 8}{5} = \dfrac{80}{5} = \textbf{16}$

(b) Total number of students = 5 × 40 = 200

Percentage of total that wear glasses = $\dfrac{80}{200}$ × 100% = **40%**

(c) Number of students in 6B that don't wear glasses = 40 – 28 = 12

Percent that do not wear glasses = $\dfrac{12}{40}$ × 100% = **30%**

📖 **Workbook Review 2**

Unit 5 – Speed

Part 1 – Speed and Average Speed

(1) Speed (pp. 74-76)

➤ Interpret speed as the rate of distance traveled per unit of time.
➤ Read and write units of speed.
➤ Find distance given the speed
➤ Find speed given distance and time.

Speed is a special kind of rate: the rate of distance covered per unit of time.

$$\text{Speed} = \frac{\text{Distance}}{\text{Time}}$$

If the speed of the vehicle remains the same over an interval of time, then it is traveling at a uniform speed. Other terms can be used, such as steady speed, constant speed, fixed speed, or given speed.

We write units of speed as km/h, m/min, m/s, cm/s, etc.

Students can regard speed as a rate which involves distance and time, and solve speed problems in the same way as rate problems. In the text and workbook, students will be given two of the three quantities, speed, time, or distance, and asked to find a third.

Since speed is distance per unit of time, we can find speed when we are given the distance and time by dividing distance by time.

A train traveled for 240 km in 4 h. What was its speed?

$$\text{Speed} = \frac{\text{Distance}}{\text{Time}} = \frac{240}{4} \text{ km/h} = 60 \text{ km/h}$$

As a rate problem, we could solve this using rate diagrams:

4 h ⟶ 240 km   4 h ⟶ 240 km

1 h ⟶ ? km   1 h ⟶ $\frac{240}{4}$ km = 60 km

The speed is 60 km/h.

In this diagram, we put the time to the left of the arrow because we know the new time (1 h), and we put the quantity we want to find to the right of the arrow. To go from 4 h to 1 h we divide by 4, so to go from 240 km to the new distance we also divide by 4.

When we are told the speed, we are given the relationship between the two quantities, distance and time. From this information, if we are given a different quantity for either the distance or the time, we can determine the corresponding time or distance, respectively.

A train traveled for 4 h at an average speed of 60 km/h. How far did it travel?

Here, we are given a new time. So we put the time first.

$$1 \text{ h} \longrightarrow 60 \text{ km}$$
$$4 \text{ h} \longrightarrow 60 \times 4 = 240 \text{ km}$$
The train traveled 240 km.

Or we can use the formula:

Distance = Speed $\times$ Time = 60 km/h $\times$ 4 h = 240 km

How long will it take a train to travel 240 km at an average speed of 60 km/h?

In using an arrow diagram to solve this, put the quantity for which have a new value first.

60 km $\longrightarrow$ 1 h	Steps can be combined:
1 km $\longrightarrow \dfrac{1}{60}$ h	60 km $\longrightarrow$ 1 h
240 km $\longrightarrow \dfrac{1}{60} \times 240$ h = 4 h	240 km $\longrightarrow \dfrac{1}{60} \times 240 = 4$ h

We first find the time for 1 km, then for 240 km, similar to the unitary approach learned in the last unit for percentage problems.

The time taken was 4 h.
We can also solve this problem using the formula:

$$\text{Time} = \frac{\text{Distance}}{\text{Speed}} = \frac{240 \text{ km}}{60 \text{ km/h}} = 4 \text{ h}$$

Students can use a triangle diagram to remember the relationship between speed, distance, and time.

$$\text{Speed} = \frac{\text{Distance}}{\text{Time}}$$
$$\text{Time} = \frac{\text{Distance}}{\text{Speed}}$$
Distance = Speed $\times$ Time

Encourage your student to solve speed problems in the same way as rate problems. This allows your student to use the concept of rate, and not be dependent on memorizing formulas or exactly how to draw and label the triangle diagram.

Your student is probably familiar with the concept of speed. Discuss instances where speed is used, such as the speed of a car, the speed at which a cheetah runs, etc. Sometime when taking a trip in the car point out the speedometer and have your student read it and see how the needle moves or gauge increases or decreases as the car speeds up or slows down.

 Page 74

Discuss this page. Make sure your student knows how to read the speedometer.

Remind your student that a rate compares two quantities with different units. Discuss some examples of rate, such as glasses of water that should be drunk per day, amount of rainfall per year, etc. Note that rates are generally given as some amount in one measurement unit per 1 of the other measurement unit. Speed is a type of rate. Draw rate diagrams for the information at the bottom of the page:

$$1\ h \longrightarrow 75\ km$$
$$2\ h \longrightarrow 75 \times 2 = 150\ km$$
$$3\ h \longrightarrow 75 \times 3 = \mathbf{225}\ km$$

 Learning Tasks 1-4, pp. 75-76

 1.

50 km/h	**65 km/h**	**35 km/h**
90 mi/h	**45 mi/h**	**70 mi/h**
90 km /h	**45 km /h**	**70 km /h**

US›

3d›

US› 2.   In 1 h, the van can travel 50 miles.
$$1\ h \longrightarrow 50\ mi$$
$$2\ h \longrightarrow 50 \times 2 = \mathbf{100}\ mi$$
It can travel **100** miles in 2 hours.

3d› 2.   In 1 h, the van can travel 50 kilometers.
$$1\ h \longrightarrow 50\ km$$
$$2\ h \longrightarrow 50 \times 2 = \mathbf{100}\ km$$
$$\text{Speed (50 km/h)} \times \text{Time (2 h)} = \text{Distance (100 km)}$$
It can travel **100** kilometers in 2 hours.

3.   In 1 min, Eric can swim 40 meters.
$$1\ min \longrightarrow 40\ m \qquad \text{Distance} = \text{Speed} \times \text{Time}$$
$$5\ min \longrightarrow 40 \times 5 = \mathbf{200}\ m \qquad = 40\ m/min \times 5\ min = 200\ m$$
He can swim **200** m in 5 min.

Note that we can derive the formula for finding distance given speed and time (Distance = Speed × Time) from the rate method.

4. In 2 seconds, the bullet travels 420 m.

$$2 \text{ s} \longrightarrow 420 \text{ m}$$

$$1 \text{ s} \longrightarrow \frac{420}{2} = \mathbf{210} \text{ m}$$

$$\frac{\text{Distance (420 m)}}{\text{Time (2 s)}} = \text{Speed (210 m/s)}$$

Its speed is **210** m/s.

5. In 30 s, he runs 150 m.

$$30 \text{ s} \longrightarrow 150 \text{ m}$$

$$1 \text{ s} \longrightarrow \frac{150}{30} = \mathbf{5} \text{ m}$$

Ravi's speed is **5** m/s

$$\text{Speed} = \frac{\text{Distance}}{\text{Time}}$$

$$= \frac{150 \text{ m}}{30 \text{ s}} = 5 \text{ m/s}$$

Note that we can derive the formula for finding speed given distance and time and time (Speed = Distance ÷ Time) from the rate method.

Practice 5A, p. 81, problems 1-3
You can use these problems for additional learning tasks, if necessary. Answers are on p. 90.

Workbook Exercise 27

---

(2) Average Speed (pp. 76-77)

➢ Understand average speed.
➢ Find average speed given distance and time.
➢ Find time given average speed and distance

If the speed of an object, such as a vehicle, remains the same, or constant, over a period of time, we say that the vehicle is traveling at a uniform speed, or constant speed, or steady speed. Using cruise control in a vehicle keeps a car at a steady speed without having to use the accelerator.

Usually, the speed of a vehicle varies during a trip, so when we divide the total distance covered during the trip by the time taken we get the average speed for the trip.

➤ Discuss the concept of average speed with your student. For example, when we drive a car, even on a highway, we do not always go at the same speed. We might speed up to pass, or slow down before passing. But if we go a total distance of 60 miles (or kilometers) in one hour, we can say that the *average* speed was 60 mi/h (or km/h). For 5 minutes we might have been going 70 miles per hour, and for another five minutes 50 miles per hours, but in those 10 minutes we will have traveled the same distance as if we went 60 miles per hour for all 10 minutes. So we can say that our average speed during those ten minutes was 60 miles per hour.

Average speed is the speed at which we would get the same distance in the same amount of time as we would if we went faster during parts of the trip and slower during other parts of the trip.

➤ Look up the distance from your location to some towns or places your student may have visited by car. Estimate the time it took to get to those places and have your student find the average speed.

 Learning Tasks 6-7, pp. 76-77

 6.   Average speed = $\dfrac{\text{Distance}}{\text{Time}}$ = $\dfrac{220}{4}$ = **55** km/h

7.   Average speed = $\dfrac{\text{Distance}}{\text{Time}}$ = $\dfrac{534}{6}$ = **89** m/min

---

➤ Tell your student that so far, we have found speed given the distance and time, and distance given the speed and time. Now we will find the time, given the distance and speed. Give your student the following problem, or a similar problem.

A train traveled 240 km at an average speed of 60 km/h. What was the time taken?

The speed tells us that we have a rate of 60 km for every hour. We want to find the time it takes to go 240 km at that speed. We can solve this like a rate problem. Since we know the new distance, but need to find a new time, we set up the rate problem with the distance first:

> 60 km ⟶ 1 h
> 240 km ⟶ ? h

Ask your student how she would find the new time. She may notice that since the distance is 4 times as much, the time would also be 4 times as much.

> x4 ⟮ 60 km ⟶ 1 h
> 240 km ⟶ 1 × 4 h ⟯ x4

It takes 4 hours to go 240 km.

Tell her that we can also use a unitary approach, similar to what we did with percentage problem. We can first find how long it would take him to go 1 km.

In using an arrow diagram to solve this, put the quantity for which have a new value first.

$$60 \text{ km} \longrightarrow 1 \text{ h}$$

$$1 \text{ km} \longrightarrow \frac{1}{60} \text{ h}$$

$$240 \text{ km} \longrightarrow \frac{1}{60} \times 240 \text{ h} = 4 \text{ h}$$

The expression, $\frac{1}{60} \times 240$, can be rewritten as $\frac{240}{60}$. This is the distance divided by the speed. So Time $= \dfrac{\text{Distance}}{\text{Speed}} = \dfrac{240 \text{ km}}{60 \text{ km/h}} = 4 \text{ h}.$

➤ List the three equations that have been learned so far, and draw a distance-speed-time triangle:

$$\text{Speed} = \frac{\text{Distance}}{\text{Time}}$$

$$\text{Time} = \frac{\text{Distance}}{\text{Speed}}$$

$$\text{Distance} = \text{Speed} \times \text{Time}$$

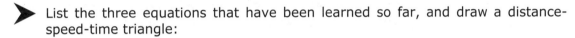

Show your student how he can come up with the equations from the triangle diagram. Point out that if he forgets the equations or how to draw the triangle, he can always use the rate method to solve the problem.

  Learning Tasks 8-9, p. 77

8. $70 \text{ km} \longrightarrow 1 \text{ h}$

$245 \text{ km} \longrightarrow \dfrac{1}{70} \times 245$ or: Time $= \dfrac{\text{Distance}}{\text{Speed}}$

$= \mathbf{3\dfrac{1}{2}} \text{ h}$ $= \dfrac{245 \text{ km}}{70 \text{ km/h}} = 3\dfrac{1}{2} \text{ h}$

9. $90 \text{ m} \longrightarrow 1 \text{ min}$

$720 \text{ m} \longrightarrow \dfrac{1}{90} \times 720$ or: Time $= \dfrac{\text{Distance}}{\text{Speed}}$

$= \mathbf{8} \text{ min}$ $= \dfrac{720 \text{ m}}{90 \text{ m/min}} = 8 \text{ min}$

Practice 5A, p. 81, problems 4 and 10
You can use these problems for additional learning tasks, if necessary.
Answers are on p. 90.

 Workbook Exercise 28

(3) Word Problems I (pp. 77-78)

 ➢ Solve 2-step word problems involving speed.

 Diagrams are helpful in solving word problems involving speed because they can be labeled with pertinent information. These are usually drawn as a line between two places, and the any information known about the distance, time, and speed marked. They will be particularly useful for multi-step problems.

 Learning Task 10, p. 77
For learning tasks 11-12, point out to your student how we can gather the information given in the problem in a diagram, which allows us to see the important information in one spot without the words of the problem interfering. Have him associate the information in the written problem with the information on the diagrams.

 10. (b) **11:00**

11. **5** h

12. **49** km/h

 Practice 5A, p. 81, problems 5-9
You can use these problems for additional learning tasks, if necessary.
Answers are on p. 90.

 Workbook Exercise 29

(4) Word Problems II (p. 79)

 ➢ Solve multi-step word problems involving two parts traveled at different speeds.

 In order to find the average speed for a trip that is divided into two parts, the student must find the total distance traveled and the total time taken. It is not possible to simply average the two speeds for each part of the trip, even if the distance is the same.

For example, a car travels for 180 km at 90 km/h and for another 180 km at 60 km/h. The average speed is not the average of 90 km/h and 60 km/h (75 km/h).

For the first part of the journey, the car traveled for 2 h, and for the second, it traveled for 3 h. The total time is 5 h. The total distance is 360 km. The average speed is $\dfrac{360 \text{ km}}{5 \text{ h}}$, or 72 km/h.

Hour 1	90 km/h
Hour 2	90 km/h
Hour 3	60 km/h
Hour 4	60 km/h
Hour 5	60 km/h
Average	$\dfrac{90 + 90 + 60 + 60 + 60}{5} = \dfrac{360}{5} = 72$ km/h

In discussing the word problems in this and the following section, you can ask your student pertinent questions to lead him to the solution. You can also write the problem on a white-board or paper and have your student draw the diagram himself before looking at the solution in the text. Or, you can draw the diagram as you discuss it.

 Learning Tasks 13-14, p. 79

13. What is the question? To find the average speed.
    What do we need to know to find the average speed? We need to know the total distance and time. How can we find the total distance? (Draw a line showing the total distance.) Speed and time are given for both parts of the trip, so the distance can be found for each part. (Label the speed and time for each part of the trip, and label what needs to be found.)
    Total distance traveled = (80 km/h × 2 h) + (70 km/h × 3 h) = **370** km
    How can we find the total time? It is the sum of the time for the two parts of the trip.

 Total time taken = 2 h + 3 h = **5** h

Average speed = $\dfrac{370 \text{ km}}{5 \text{ h}}$ = **74** km/h

14. Total distance traveled = 36 km + 96 km = **132** km

Total time taken = $\dfrac{36 \text{ km}}{54 \text{ km/h}} + \dfrac{96 \text{ km}}{72 \text{ km/h}} = \dfrac{2}{3}$ h $+ \dfrac{4}{3}$ h = **2** h

Average speed = $\dfrac{132 \text{ km}}{2 \text{ h}}$ = **66** km/h

---

 Workbook Exercise 30

---

(5) Word Problems III (p. 80)

 ➢   Solve multi-step word problems involving speed

 The problems in this section involve at least three distances — the first part of the trip, the second part of the trip, and the total trip. The student will have to use the information from the two of the other distances to find the time, distance, and/or speed for the third distance. These problems are somewhat challenging. Try to get your student to draw the picture and label it rather than just showing him the one in the text.

 Learning Tasks 15-16, p. 80
In these tasks, ask your student what information we first need to find in order to solve the problem.

 15. To find the average speed, we need to find the total distance and the total time. How do we find the total distance?

We know the distance for $\dfrac{1}{3}$ of the trip. From this we can find the total distance.

$\dfrac{1}{3}$ of the distance = 120 km

$\dfrac{3}{3}$ of the distance = 120 × 3 = 360 km

The total distance traveled = **360** km
How do we find the total time? We are given the time for both parts, so we can add to find the total time.
Total time taken = 3 h + 2 h = **5** h

Average speed = $\dfrac{360 \text{ km}}{5 \text{ h}}$ = **72** km/h

16. To find the average speed for the remaining trip, we need to find the remaining distance and time.
    We can find the total distance from the average speed and the time for the entire trip. (240 km)
    Since we know the fraction of the distance each part is of the entire trip, we can find the distance for the second part.

    $\frac{1}{5}$ of the trip = $\frac{1}{5}$ × 240 km = **48** km

    We now need to find the time for the second part.
    We know the time for the total trip. We know the speed for the first part. If we find the distance for the first part, we can find the time for the first part, and subtract from the total time to find the time for the second part.

    $\frac{4}{5}$ of the trip = 240 km – 48 km = **192** km (or 4 × 48 km = 192 km)

    Time taken for the first part = $\dfrac{192 \text{ km}}{64 \text{ km/h}}$ = **3** h

    Time taken for the remaining part = 4 h – 3 h = **1** h

    Average speed for remaining part = $\dfrac{48 \text{ km}}{1 \text{ h}}$ = **48** km/h

---

 Workbook Exercise 31

Practice (pp. 81-82)

 ➤ Solve word problems involving speed.

 Practice 5A, p. 81

 1. Speed = $\dfrac{50 \text{ m}}{40 \text{ s}}$ = **1.25 m/s**

2. Speed = $\dfrac{450 \text{ cm}}{15 \text{ s}}$ = **30 cm/s**

US› 3. Distance = Speed × Time = 420 mi/h × 3 h = **1260 mi**
3d› 3. Distance = Speed × Time = 420 km/h × 3 h = **1260 km**

4. Time = $\dfrac{\text{Distance}}{\text{Speed}}$ = $\dfrac{300 \text{ m}}{6 \text{ m/s}}$ = **50 s**

5. 8:30   100 km/h

   X ├─────────────────────────────┤ Y

   Time = $\dfrac{\text{Distance}}{\text{Speed}}$ = $\dfrac{250 \text{ km}}{100 \text{ km/h}}$ = $2\dfrac{1}{2}$ h

   Time of arrival = 8:30 a.m. + $2\dfrac{1}{2}$ h = **11:00 a.m.**

6. Find the total distance using (**US›** Ryan's, **3d›** Ravi's) speed and time.
   Distance to school = 15 min × 70 m/min
                                      = 1050 m
   Brother's speed = $\dfrac{1050 \text{ m}}{20 \text{ min}}$ = **52.5 m/min**

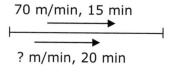

7. Distance to town = 60 km/h × 2 h = 120 km
   Time at new speed = $\dfrac{120 \text{ km}}{80 \text{ km/h}}$ = $1\dfrac{1}{2}$ h

8. Total distance run = 400 m × 4 = 1,600 m
   Average speed = $\dfrac{1600 \text{ m}}{8 \text{ min}}$ = **200 m/min**

9. Total time = 11:30 a.m. – 9:30 a.m. = 2 h
   Distance = Speed × Time = 60 km/h × 2 h = **120 km**

10. Time = $\dfrac{\text{Distance}}{\text{Speed}}$ = $\dfrac{720 \text{ m}}{80 \text{ m/min}}$ = **9 min**

Practice 5B p. 82

1. Total time = 4:30 − 2:30 = 2 h
   Total distance = 22.5 km + 42.8 km + 42.7 km = 108 km
   Average speed = $\dfrac{108 \text{ km}}{2 \text{ h}}$ = **54 km/h**

2. (a) Distance between the towns = 10 km/h × 2 h = **20 km**

   (b) New speed = 10 km/h + 2 km/h = 12 km/h
   New time = $\dfrac{\text{Distance}}{\text{New speed}}$ = $\dfrac{20 \text{ km}}{12 \text{ km/h}}$ = $1\frac{2}{3}$ h = **1 h 40 min**

3. David's time = $\dfrac{24 \text{ km}}{9 \text{ km/h}}$
   = $2\frac{2}{3}$ h

   Ben's time = $2\frac{2}{3}$ h + 20 min = $2\frac{2}{3}$ h + $\frac{1}{3}$ h = 3 h

   Ben's speed = $\dfrac{24 \text{ km}}{3 \text{ h}}$ = **8 km/h**

4. House   Road   Office
   5 min   10 min
   46 m/min   40 m/min

   Total distance = (46 m/min × 5 min) + (40 m/min × 10 min)
   = 230 m + 400 m
   = **630 m**

5. Distance for second part
   = 12 km − 3 km = 9 km
   Total time = $\dfrac{3 \text{ km}}{4 \text{ km/h}}$ + $\dfrac{9 \text{ km}}{6 \text{ km/h}}$

   12 km
   3 km   6 km/h
   4 km/h

   = $\dfrac{3}{4}$ h + $\dfrac{6}{4}$ h = $2\frac{1}{4}$ h = **2 h 15 min**

6. (a) $\dfrac{1}{5}$ of the distance = 30 km

   X   Y
   2 h   1 h
   30 km

   $\dfrac{5}{5}$ of the distance = 30 × 5 = **150 km**

   (b) Total time = 2 h + 1 h = 3 h
   Average speed = $\dfrac{150 \text{ km}}{3 \text{ h}}$ = **50 km/h**

7.   (a) $\frac{2}{3}$ of the distance = 240 km

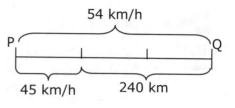

$\frac{1}{3}$ of the distance = $\frac{240}{2}$ = 120 km

$\frac{3}{3}$ of the distance = 120×3 = **360 km**

(b)   Use the total distance and average speed to find the total time.

Total time = $\dfrac{360 \text{ km}}{54 \text{ km/h}}$ = $\dfrac{20}{3}$ h

We have both speed and distance for the first part of the trip.
Find the total time for the first part of the trip.

Time for first part = $\dfrac{120 \text{ km}}{45 \text{ km/h}}$ = $\dfrac{8}{3}$ h

Find the time for the second part of the trip.

Time for second part = $\dfrac{20}{3}$ h $-\dfrac{8}{3}$ h = $\dfrac{12}{3}$ = 4 h

Use that time and the distance of the second part to find the average speed for the second half.

Average speed for second part = $\dfrac{240 \text{ km}}{4 \text{ h}}$ = **60 km/h**

Review

Review D (pp. 83-86)

1. (a) **thirty thousand, six hundred**
    (b) **two million, four hundred seventy thousand**

2. (a) **600** (b) **0.007**

3. (a) **26,327** (b) **43,469**

4. (a) **400** (b) **0.005**

5. (a) **38** (b) **200**

6. (a) **8.7** (b) **2.40**

7. **33** (3×11)

8. (a) $24 + \underline{18 \div 3} \times 2$
    $= 24 + \underline{6 \times 2}$
    $= \underline{24 + 12}$
    $= \mathbf{36}$

    (b) $\underline{(12 + 13)} \div 3 + 2 \times 4$
    $= \underline{25 \div 3} + 2 \times 4$
    $= \frac{25}{3} + \underline{2 \times 4}$
    $= 8\frac{1}{3} + 8$
    $= \mathbf{16\frac{1}{3}}$

9. (a) **10** (b) **1000**
    (c) **100** (d) **10**

10. **7** (4 quarters in 1, 3 quarters in $\frac{3}{4}$)

11. (a) **3.604** (b) $0.04 + 0.015 = \mathbf{0.055}$

12. **3.42**

13. **120 ml** (each division is 25 ml)

14. (a) 1 kg = 1000 g
    $1\frac{1}{4}$ kg = $1\frac{1}{4} \times 1000$
    $= 1000 + 250$
    $= \mathbf{1250}$ g

    (b) 1 h = 60 min
    $1\frac{2}{3}$ h = $1\frac{2}{3} \times 60$
    $= 60 + 40$
    $= \mathbf{100}$ min

15. (a) 9 : 3 = 3 : **1** (b) 1 : 4 : 3 = 9 : **36** : **27**

16. (a) $\frac{15}{40} \times 100\% = \mathbf{37.5\%}$ (b) $\frac{270}{600} \times 100\% = \mathbf{45\%}$

17. (a) $0.084 = \dfrac{84}{1000} = \dfrac{\mathbf{21}}{\mathbf{250}}$ (b) $28\% = \dfrac{28}{100} = \dfrac{\mathbf{7}}{\mathbf{25}}$

18. $\dfrac{1.4}{2} \times 100\% = \mathbf{70\%}$

19. (a) $\dfrac{15}{100} \times 900 = \mathbf{135}$ (b) $\dfrac{3}{10} \times 4800 = \mathbf{1440}$

20. (a) $15 : 3 : 12 = \mathbf{5 : 1 : 4}$ (b) $\dfrac{\text{compact disc}}{\text{total}} = \dfrac{15}{30} = \dfrac{5}{10} = \dfrac{\mathbf{1}}{\mathbf{2}}$

    (c) $\mathbf{50\%}$

21. $\mathbf{4 : 3}$

22. $\dfrac{3}{5} \times 100\% = \mathbf{60\%}$

23. $5 \longrightarrow \$1.20$

     $60 \longrightarrow \$\dfrac{1.20}{5} \times 60 = \$14.40$

     He received $\mathbf{\$14.40}$.

24. $\$12 \longrightarrow 8$

     $\$15 \longrightarrow \dfrac{8}{12} \times 15 = 10$

     $\mathbf{10}$ mangoes will cost $15.

25. $100 \text{ g} \longrightarrow \$0.15$

     $600 \text{ g} \longrightarrow \$\dfrac{0.15}{100} \times 600 = \$0.90$

     600 g of bananas cost $\mathbf{\$0.90}$.

26. Cost for printing 35 pictures $= \$0.25 \times 35 = \$8.75$

     Cost for roll and pictures $= \$3 + \$8.75 = \mathbf{\$11.75}$

27. Fraction of total money spent $= \dfrac{3}{5} + \dfrac{1}{6} = \dfrac{18}{30} + \dfrac{5}{30} = \dfrac{23}{30}$

     Fraction of money left $= 1 - \dfrac{23}{30} = \dfrac{7}{30}$

     $\dfrac{7}{30}$ of the money $= \$14$

     $\dfrac{30}{30}$ of the money $= \$\dfrac{14}{7} \times 30 = \$60$

     She had $\mathbf{\$60}$ at first.

28. 2 units = 20

  1 unit $= \dfrac{20}{2}$

  8 units $= \dfrac{20}{2} \times 8 = 80$

  There are **80** children.

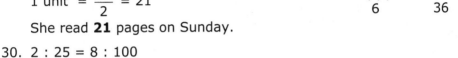

29. $\dfrac{1}{4}$ of the book = 1 unit

  2 units $= 36 + 6 = 42$

  1 unit $= \dfrac{42}{2} = 21$

  She read **21** pages on Sunday.

30. 2 : 25 = 8 : 100

  If there are 8 teachers, there are **100** students.

31. length : width = 3 : 2 = 9 : 6

  If the length is 9 cm, then the width is 6 cm.

  Area = 9 cm × 6 cm = **54 cm²**.

32. 3 units = $240

  1 unit $= \$\dfrac{240}{3} = \$80$

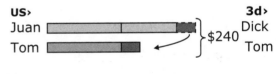

  $(2 \times \$80) - \$20 = \$140$

  $\$80 + \$20 = \$100$

  New ratio = 140 : 100 = **7 : 5**

33. Remainder after giving $400 to parents = $850 − $400 = $450

  Percentage of remainder left after spending 40% of remainder = 60%

  60% of $450 $= \dfrac{6}{10} \times \$450 = \$270$

  She had **$270** left.

34. 40% of her money = $28

  1% of her money $= \$\dfrac{28}{40}$

  100% of her money $= \$\dfrac{28}{40} \times 100 = \$70$

  She had **$70** at first.

35. 10 minutes $= \dfrac{1}{6}$ h

  Distance = 3 km/h $\times \dfrac{1}{6}$ h $= \dfrac{1}{2}$ km = **500 m**

36. Time $= \dfrac{\text{Distance}}{\text{Speed}} = \dfrac{240 \text{ km}}{80 \text{ km/h}} = 3$ h

8:10 a.m. $+ 3$ h $= 11$:10 a.m
He arrived at **11:10 a.m.**

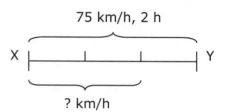
75 km/h, 2 h

X ————— Y

? km/h

37. (a) Distance $= 75$ km/h $\times 2$ h $= 150$ km
Distance Pablo traveled in 2 h

$= \dfrac{2}{3} \times 150 = 100$ km

Pablo's speed $= \dfrac{100 \text{ km}}{2 \text{ h}} =$ **50 km/h**

(b) Distance for last third $= 50$ km
Speed for last third $= 50 + 10 = 60$ km/h

Time $= \dfrac{\text{Distance}}{\text{Speed}} = \dfrac{50 \text{ km}}{60 \text{ km/h}} = \dfrac{5}{6}$ h $= \dfrac{5}{6} \times 60$ min $=$ **50 min**

38. (a) **B**   (b) $24 : 28 =$ **6 : 7**

(c) Number more students $= 26 - 20 = 6$

Percent more students $= \dfrac{6}{20} \times 100\% =$ **30%**

Review E, pp. 87–92

1. (a) **10,000**   (b) **0.4**

2. (a) $\underline{(59 + 13)} \div \underline{(4 \times 2)}$
$= \underline{72 \div 8}$
$= $ **9**

(b) $18 \div \underline{(6 + 3)} \times 2$
$= \underline{18 \div 9} \times 2$
$= \underline{2 \times 2}$
$= $ **4**

3. **4.501 km**

4. $\dfrac{348}{24} = \dfrac{58}{4} = \dfrac{29}{2} = \dfrac{28}{2} + \dfrac{1}{2} =$ **14.5**

5. $\dfrac{1}{2}$ of $\dfrac{1}{4} + \dfrac{1}{2}$ of $\dfrac{1}{4} = \dfrac{2}{8} = \dfrac{\mathbf{1}}{\mathbf{4}}$

or: Slide the bottom triangle over; it fits below the top triangle, and both

take up $\dfrac{1}{4}$ of the rectangle.

6. (a) **5**   (b) **1000**

7. Fraction saved $= \dfrac{400}{2400} = \dfrac{\mathbf{1}}{\mathbf{6}}$

8. (a) $1\frac{1}{3}$ h $= 1\frac{1}{3} \times 60$ min

    $= 60 + 20$ min

    $= \textbf{1 h 20 min}$

    (b) $2.67\ \ell = 2\ \ell + 0.67 \times 1{,}000$ ml

    $= \textbf{2 } \ell \textbf{ 670 ml}$

9. (a) $\frac{7}{10}$ m $= \frac{7}{10} \times 100$ cm

    $= \textbf{70}$ cm

    (b) $\frac{4}{5}$ kg $= \frac{4}{5} \times 1{,}000$ g

    $= \textbf{800}$ g

    (c) $2\frac{3}{10}$ ml $= 2\frac{3}{10} \times 1{,}000$ ml

    $= 2{,}000 + 300$

    $= \textbf{2,300}$ ml

    (d) $1\frac{1}{2}$ h $= 1\frac{1}{2}$ h $\times 60$ min

    $= 60 + 30$

    $= \textbf{90}$ min

10. $2\frac{5}{8} = 2.625 \approx \textbf{2.63}$

11. $\dfrac{2.74 + 1.9 + 3.04}{3} = \dfrac{7.68}{3} = 2.56 \approx \textbf{2.6 kg}$

12. Percent with computers $= \dfrac{320}{500} \times 100\% = \textbf{64\%}$

13. $\dfrac{1}{40} \times 100\% = \textbf{2.5\%}$

14. $\$1.50 \longrightarrow 6$ pears

    $\$1 \longrightarrow \dfrac{6}{1.50}$ pears

    $\$9 \longrightarrow \dfrac{6}{1.50} \times 9 = \textbf{36}$ pears

15. 100 g $\longrightarrow \$0.72$

    1 g $\longrightarrow \$\dfrac{0.72}{100}$

    450 g $\longrightarrow \$\dfrac{0.72}{100} \times 450 = \textbf{\$3.24}$

16. (a) # green : # yellow = **4 : 5**

    (b) $\dfrac{\text{\# yellow}}{\text{\# green}} = \dfrac{\textbf{5}}{\textbf{4}}$

    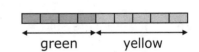
    green   yellow

17. Draw a model:

    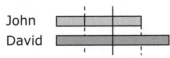
    John
    David

    David's : John's = **3 : 4**

    or:

    $\dfrac{2}{3}$ of David's $= \dfrac{1}{2}$ of John's

    $\dfrac{1}{3}$ of David's $= \dfrac{1}{2} \div 2 = \dfrac{1}{4}$ of John's

    $\dfrac{3}{3}$ David's $= \dfrac{1}{4} \times 3 = \dfrac{3}{4}$ of John's

    David's : John's = 3 : 4

18. $0.15 $\longrightarrow$ 1 egg

   $1 $\longrightarrow$ $\dfrac{1}{0.15} = \dfrac{100}{15}$ eggs

   $3 $\longrightarrow$ $\dfrac{100}{15} \times 3 =$ **20** eggs

19. 4 cakes $\longrightarrow$ 480 g

   1 cake $\longrightarrow$ $\dfrac{480}{4}$ g

   3 cakes $\longrightarrow$ $\dfrac{480}{4} \times 3 =$ **360 g**

20. 3 oranges $\longrightarrow$ $2

   1 orange $\longrightarrow$ $$\dfrac{2}{3}$

   12 oranges $\longrightarrow$ $$\dfrac{2}{3} \times 12 =$ **$8**

21. Cost of exercise books = $8 \times \$0.55 = \$4.40$
    Amount spent = $\$10 - \$2.05 = \$7.95$
    Cost of file = amount spent – cost of exercise books
    $\qquad = \$7.95 - \$4.40 =$ **$3.55**

22. Find the amount earned from each group of 30 magazines he sold.
    $(\$0.40 \times 30) + \$3 = \$15$
    Find the number of groups of 30 he sold.
    $\$450 \div \$15 = 30$
    He sold 30 groups of 30 magazines.
    Total number of magazines sold = $30 \times 30 =$ **900**

23. Weight of 12 eggs = weight of tray with eggs – weight of tray
    $\qquad\qquad\qquad = 440 \text{ g} - 20 \text{ g} = 420 \text{ g}$

    Average weight of 1 egg = $\dfrac{420}{12}$ g = **35 g**

24. (a) Total cars sold = $8 \times 4.5 = 36$

   Average for 12 months = $\dfrac{36}{12} =$ **3 cars**

   (b) Money received = $\$800 \times 36 =$ **$28,800**

25. Length of lace used = $12 - 4\dfrac{4}{5} = 8 - \dfrac{4}{5} =$ **$7\dfrac{1}{5}$** m

26. Height = $\dfrac{3}{5} \times 25 =$ **15 cm**

27.

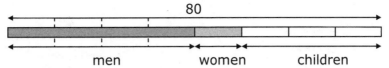

80

men   women   children

16 units = 80
  1 unit = 5
There are 10 units of adults and
6 units of children. 10 – 6 = 4
  4 units = 5 × 4 = 20
There are **20** more adults than
children.

or:

Number of men = $\frac{1}{2} \times 80 = 40$

Remainder = 80 – 40 = 40

Number of women = $\frac{1}{4} \times 40 = 10$

Number of children = 40 – 10 = 30
Total adults = 40 + 10 = 50
Adults – children = 50 – 30 = 20

US› 28. Nicoles's earnings = $\frac{4}{5}$ of Sean's earnings = $\frac{4}{5} \times \$2600 = \$2080$

Total earnings = $2600 + $2080 = $4680

Amount saved = $\frac{1}{3}$ of total earnings = $\frac{1}{3} \times \$4680 =$ **$1560**

3d› 28. Mrs. Li's earnings = $\frac{4}{5}$ of Mr Li's's earnings = $\frac{4}{5} \times \$2600 = \$2080$

Total earnings = $2600 + $2080 = $4680

Amount saved = $\frac{1}{3}$ of total earnings = $\frac{1}{3} \times \$4680 =$ **$1560**

29.

weight of bottle   weight of water

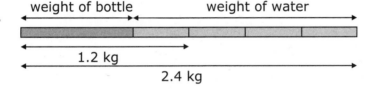

1.2 kg

2.4 kg

3 units of water = 2.4 – 1.2 = 1.2 kg

1 unit of water = $\frac{1.2}{3} = 0.4$ kg

weight of bottle = weight of bottle with 1 unit of water – weight of 1 unit of water
                          = 1.2 – 0.4 = **0.8 kg**

30. 12 units = $300

   1 unit = $\$\frac{300}{12}$

   2 units = $\$\frac{300}{12} \times 2 = \$50$

Peter received **$50** more than David.

Peter
David
$300
?

31. Number of children stays the same.
    adults : children
    Before   8 : 3 = 8 : 3
    After   2 : 1 = 6 : 3
    2 units of adults leave.
    2 units = 10
    3 units = $\dfrac{10}{2} \times 3 = 15$
    There are **15** children on the ferry.

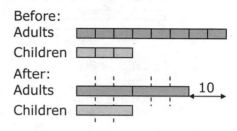

Before:
Adults
Children
After:
Adults   10
Children

32. (a) John : David
        3 : 4
            David : Paul
             2 : 1
           = 4 : 2
        John : David : Paul
        3 :   4 : 2

John
David
Paul
$60

(b) 2 units = $60
    1 unit = $\dfrac{60}{2}$
    3 units = $\dfrac{60}{2} \times 3 = \$90$
    John has **$90**.

33. 100% is 40 books.
    100% → 40
    1% → $\dfrac{40}{100}$

    125% → $\dfrac{40}{100} \times 125 = 50$

    Steven has **50** books.

34. Percentage decrease = $\dfrac{4000 - 2800}{4000} \times 100\% = \dfrac{1200}{4000} \times 100\% = $ **30%**

35. Percent more = $\dfrac{500 - 400}{400} \times 100\% = \dfrac{100}{400} \times 100\% = $ **25%**

36. Remainder after cakes = 100% − 30% = 70%
    40% of 70% = $\dfrac{4}{10} \times 70\% = 28\%$
    Total percentage used = 30% + 28% = **58%**

37. 30% of the girls is 54.

$30\% \longrightarrow 54$

$1\% \longrightarrow \dfrac{54}{30}$

$230\% \longrightarrow \dfrac{54}{30} \times 230 = 414$

There are **414** children.

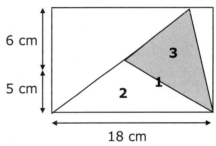

38. Time $= \dfrac{\text{Distance}}{\text{Speed}} = \dfrac{150 \text{ km}}{60 \text{ km/h}} = 2\dfrac{1}{2}$ h = 2 h 30 min

11:30 a.m. – 2 h 30 min = 9:00 a.m.

He left Town P at **9:00 a.m.**

39. Distance for first part of the trip
   = 75 km/h × 2 h = 150 km
   Total distance = 150 × 2 = 300 km

   Total time = $\dfrac{300 \text{ km}}{60 \text{ km/h}}$ = 5 h

   Time for last part = 5 h – 2 h = 3 h

   Speed for last part = $\dfrac{150 \text{ km}}{3 \text{ h}}$ = **50 km/h**

60 km/h

A |——————|——————| B

75 km/h, 2 h   ? km/h

40. Area of △ 1 = $\dfrac{1}{2} \times 18 \times 11 = 99$ cm^2

   Area of △ 2 = $\dfrac{1}{2} \times 18 \times 5 = 45$ cm^2

   Area of △ 3 = area of △ 1 – area of △ 2
       = 99 – 45 = **54 cm²**

6 cm
5 cm
18 cm

41. (a)   (b)

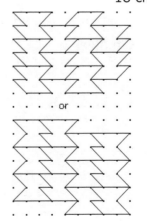

or

42. **36**

43. (a) Average $= \dfrac{1500 + 4000 + 2000 + 4500}{4} = \dfrac{12,000}{4} = \mathbf{3000}$

   (b) Increase $= 4500 - 2,000 = \mathbf{2500}$

   (c) Number sold in July $= 4,000$
   Amount received $= \$0.40 \times 4,000 = \mathbf{\$1600}$

 US› Review F, pp. 93-96

1. (a) 26 oz $= 16$ oz $+ 10$ oz $= \mathbf{1\ lb\ 10\ oz}$
   (b) 38 oz $= 32$ oz $+ 6$ oz $= \mathbf{2\ lb\ 6\ oz}$
   (c) 17 oz $= 16$ oz $+ 1$ oz $= \mathbf{1\ lb\ 1\ oz}$

2. Total units $= 7$; 7 units $= 161$ lb, 1 unit $= 161$ lb $\div 7 = 23$ lb
   (a) Mary's weight $= 3$ units $= 23$ lb $\times 3 = \mathbf{69\ lb}$
   (b) Aly's weight $= 4$ units $= 23$ lb $\times 4 = \mathbf{92\ lb}$

3. 3 units $= 6$ ft 3 in. 1 unit $= 2$ ft 1 in.
   Juan's height $= 2$ ft 1 in. $\times 2 = \mathbf{4\ ft\ 2\ in.}$

4. $3\frac{1}{4}$ lb $= 3\frac{1}{4} \times 16$ oz $= 48$ oz $+ 4$ oz $= 52$ oz; $\mathbf{3\frac{1}{4}}$ **lb** is heavier.

   $1\frac{2}{3}$ ft $= 12$ in. $+ 8$ in. $= 20$ in; **21 in.** is longer.

   $2\frac{1}{2}$ gal $= 32$ c $+ 8$ c $= 40$ c; $\mathbf{2\frac{1}{2}}$ **gal** is more.

   $\frac{1}{3}$ yd $= 1$ ft $= 12$ in.; $\mathbf{\frac{1}{3}}$ **yd** in shorter.

5. (a) 5 yd 1 ft $\div 2 = (4$ yd $+ 3$ ft $+ 1$ ft$) \div 2$
   $= (4$ yd $\div 2) + (4$ ft $\div 2)$
   $= \mathbf{2}$ yd $\mathbf{2}$ ft

   (b) 13 lb 8 oz $\div 6 = (12$ lb $+ 16$ oz $+ 8$ oz$) \div 6$
   $= (12$ lb $\div 6) + (24$ oz $\div 6)$
   $= \mathbf{2}$ lb $\mathbf{4}$ oz

   (c) 19 gal 2 qt $\div 3 = (18$ gal $+ 4$ qt $+ 2$ qt$) \div 3$
   $= (18$ gal $\div 3) + (6$ qt $\div 3)$
   $= \mathbf{6}$ gal $\mathbf{2}$ qt

   (d) 5 ft 10 in. $\div 7 = (60$ ft $+ 10$ ft$) \div 7$
   $= 70$ ft $\div 7$
   $= \mathbf{10}$ ft

6. $\dfrac{620}{3} = 206$ r2; 620 ft $= \mathbf{206\ yd\ 2\ ft}$

7. Area of rectangle = 16 ft × 6 ft; Area of triangle = $\frac{1}{2}$ × 8 × 6 = 4 ft × 6 ft

    Fraction shaded = $\frac{4 \times 6}{16 \times 6}$ = **$\frac{1}{4}$**

8. (a) $4\frac{1}{4}$ lb = (4 × 16 oz) + ($\frac{1}{4}$ × 16 oz) = **68 oz**

    (b) $2\frac{2}{3}$ yd = (2 × 36 in.) + ($\frac{2}{3}$ × 36 in.) = 72 in. + 24 in. = **96 in.**

    (c) $5\frac{1}{2}$ gal = (5 × 16 c) + ($\frac{1}{2}$ × 16 c) = 80 c + 8 c = **88 c**

9. Amount for glasses = $\frac{2}{5}$ × 15 = 6 c

    Water in each glass = 6 c ÷ 3 = **2 c**

10. $2\frac{1}{4}$ lb = 36 oz. **Travis** bought **7** oz more.

11. 30 : 12 : 32 = **15 : 6 : 16**

12. Find the number of 15 mi units in 300, each 15 mi takes one gallon.
    Gallons used = 300 ÷ 15 = **20 gal**

13. (a) 7.75 lb = 7 lb + (0.75 × 16 oz) = **7 lb 12 oz**

    (b) $2\frac{5}{6}$ ft = 2 ft + ($\frac{5}{6}$ × 12 in.) = **2 ft 10 in.**

    (c) 3.5 qt = 3 qt + (0.5 × 4 c) = **3 qt 2 c**

14. 2 ft = 24 in; $\frac{6}{24}$ × 100% = **25%**

    (or, 6 in. is half of a foot, which is a fourth of 2 ft, or 25%)

15. 2 gal = 32 c $\frac{16}{32}$ × 100% = **50%**

    (or, 16 c is in 1 gal, so must be half of 2 gal = 50%)

16. Check drawing.

17. Total distance = (3.5 h × 65 mi/h)
    = (1.5 h × 60 mi/h)
    = 227.5 mi + 90 mi
    = **317.5 mi**

    3.5 h, 65 mi/h   1.5 h, 60 mi/h

    A _____|_____ B

18. Area = ($\frac{1}{2}$ × 12 × 5) + (6 × 12) + ($\frac{1}{2}$ × 12 × 8)
    = 30 + 72 + 48 = **150 in.³**

19. 3 ft × 3 ft × 3 ft = **27 ft²**

20. 122 in. is a little over 10 ft 2 in.; $3\frac{2}{3}$ yd = 11 ft. **122 in.** is shortest.

21. 8 mi in 1 h is 1 mi in $\frac{1}{8}$ h. $6 \times \frac{1}{8}$ h = $\frac{3}{4}$ h = 45 min.

    Or, $\frac{6\ mi}{8\ mi/h} = \frac{3}{4}$ h = **45 min**

22. Sugar left = 3 lb 7 oz – (4 oz × 7)
    = 3 lb 7 oz – 28 oz
    = 3 lb 7 oz – 1 lb 12 oz
    = **1 lb 11 oz**

23. $\frac{5}{7}$ of the tank holds 3.5 gal

    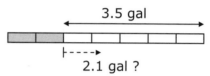

    $\frac{1}{7}$ of the tank holds 3.5 gal ÷ 5 = 0.7 gal.

    2.1 gal is $\frac{3}{7}$ of the tank.

    It is $\frac{2}{7}$ filled, adding 2.1 more gallons makes it $\frac{2}{7} + \frac{3}{7} = \frac{\mathbf{5}}{\mathbf{7}}$ filled.

24. Total traveling time = 7 h. Distance = 85 mi/h × 7 h = **595 mi.**

25. $6\frac{2}{3}$ yd = 20 ft. Percentage used = $\frac{17}{20}$ x 100% = **85%**

26. $\frac{1}{4} \longrightarrow$ 6 c; $\frac{1}{8}$ is $\frac{1}{2}$ of $\frac{1}{4}$, so $\frac{1}{8}$ holds **3 c**

27. 9 units = 27 in.
    1 unit = 27 in. ÷ 9 = 3 in.
    4 units = 3 in. × 4 = 12 in.
    width = 12 in.
    Area of unshaded part = 75% of (27 in. × 12 in.)
    $$= \frac{3}{4} \times 27 \times 12 = \mathbf{243\ in.^3}$$

 Workbook Review 3
Workbook Review 4

Solutions to Workbook Exercises and Reviews

Exercise 1

1.

   watermelon   pineapple
       m 2

   $m + 2$

   (a) $(m + 2)$kg

   (b) $m + 2 = 4 + 2$
        $= 6$ kg

   (c) $m + 6 = 6 + 2$
        $= 8$ kg

2.

   pen   book
          x

   5        $x - 5$

   (a) $\$(x - 5)$

   (b) $\$(x - 5) = \$(11 - 5)$
        $= \$6$

   (c) $\$(x - 5) = \$(15 - 5)$
        $= \$10$

3.   T-shirt
        n

   3n

   (a) $\$3n$

   (b) $\$3n = 3 \times \$8$
        $= \$24$

   (c) $\$3n = 3 \times \$10$
        $= \$30$

4. (a) $\dfrac{w}{4}$ cm

    (b) $\dfrac{w}{4} = \dfrac{592}{4}$
         $= 148$ cm

    (c) $\dfrac{w}{4} = \dfrac{608}{4}$
         $= 152$ cm

5. (a) $n + 7 = 15 + 7 = 22$

    (b) $20 - n = 20 - 15 = 5$

    (c) $3n = 3 \times 15 = 45$

    (d) $n + 5 = 15 + 5 = 20$

    (e) $\dfrac{n}{5} = \dfrac{15}{5} = 3$

    (f) $n - 3 = 15 - 3 = 12$

    (g) $\dfrac{n}{3} = \dfrac{15}{3} = 5$

    (h) $5n = 5 \times 15 = 75$

    (i) $3 + n = 3 + 15 = 18$

    (j) $\dfrac{n}{45} = \dfrac{15}{45} = \dfrac{1}{3}$

Exercise 2

1.

mango　　　　　　　　　　　　papaya

x　　x　　x　　x　　x　　x　　　5

(a) $\$(6x+5)$

(b) $6 \times 2 + 5 = 12 + 5$
$= \$17$

(c) $6 \times 3 + 5 = 18 + 5$
$= \$23$

2.

40

bottle　　　　　　　　　　y

(a) $\$\dfrac{40-y}{6}$

(b) $\dfrac{40-10}{6} = \dfrac{30}{6}$
$= \$5$

(c) $\dfrac{40-1}{6} = \dfrac{39}{6}$
$= \$6.50$

3. (a) $\dfrac{5k}{3} = \dfrac{5 \times 6}{3} = \dfrac{30}{3} = \mathbf{10}$

(b) $\dfrac{15-k}{3} = \dfrac{15-6}{3} = \dfrac{9}{3} = \mathbf{3}$

(c) $\dfrac{8+k}{7} = \dfrac{8+6}{7} = \dfrac{14}{7} = \mathbf{2}$

(d) $10 - \dfrac{2k}{3} = 10 - \dfrac{2 \times 6}{3} = 10 - 4 = \mathbf{6}$

(e) $\dfrac{k}{3} + k = \dfrac{6}{3} + 6 = 2 + 6 = \mathbf{8}$

(f) $k - \dfrac{k}{6} = 6 - \dfrac{6}{6} = 6 - 1 = \mathbf{5}$

(g) $k^2 + 4 = 6 \times 6 + 4 = 36 + 4 = \mathbf{40}$

(h) $50 - k^2 = 50 - 6 \times 6 = 50 - 36 = \mathbf{14}$

(i) $k^3 - 100 = 6 \times 6 \times 6 - 100$
$= 216 - 100$
$= \mathbf{116}$

(j) $3k^2 + 20 = 3 \times 6 \times 6 + 20$
$= 108 + 20$
$= \mathbf{128}$

Exercise 3

1. (a) $\mathbf{3x}$

(b) $\mathbf{4y}$

(c) $\mathbf{5n}$

(d) $\mathbf{6p}$

(e) $\mathbf{3x}$

(f) $\mathbf{4y}$

(g) $\mathbf{11p}$

(h) $\mathbf{2e}$

(i) $\mathbf{4a}$

(j) $\mathbf{6k}$

2. (a) $5n - 3n + 4 = \mathbf{2n + 4}$

(b) $6 + 5a - 3 = 5a + 6 - 3$
$= \mathbf{5a + 3}$

(c) $7x + 2 + 2x = 7x + 2x + 2$
$= \mathbf{9x + 2}$

(d) $4a - 2a + 5 = \mathbf{2a + 5}$

(e) $4d + 6 - 4 = \boldsymbol{4d + 2}$

(f) $18 + 6f - 9 = 6f + 18 - 9$
$$= \boldsymbol{6f + 9}$$

(g) $12 + 8h - 6h = 12 + 2h$
$$= \boldsymbol{2h + 12}$$

(h) $9a + 1 - 3a = 9a - 3a + 1$
$$= \boldsymbol{6a + 1}$$

(i) $7 + 4k - 2 - 2k$
$$= 4k - 2k + 7 - 2$$
$$= \boldsymbol{2k + 5}$$

(j) $15x + 8 - 10x - 3$
$$= 15x - 10x + 8 - 3$$
$$= \boldsymbol{5x + 5}$$

Exercise 4

2.   (a) **6**   (b) **5**   (c) **5**   (d) **4**

Exercise 5

1.   **A, C, F, G, H**   2.   **B, C, E, G, H**

Exercise 6

1.   **A, C**   2.   **A, D**   3.   **A, D**

Exercise 7

1.   **C**   2.   **C**   3.   **C**

Exercise 8

1.   (a) $42 : 63 = \boldsymbol{2 : 3}$
(factor 21)

(b) $42 : 63 : 105 = \boldsymbol{2 : 3 : 5}$
(factor 21)   •

2.   (a) John's share = $345 - $45 - 75
$$= \$225$$
$45 : 75 : 225 = \boldsymbol{3 : 5 : 15}$
(factor 15)

(b) $225 : 345 = \boldsymbol{15 : 23}$
(factor 15)

3.   (a) $6 : 8 = \boldsymbol{3 : 4}$ (factor 2)

(b) $6 : 12 = \boldsymbol{1 : 2}$ (factor 6)

(c) $8 : 12 = \boldsymbol{2 : 3}$
(factor 4)

(d) $6 : 8 : 12 = \boldsymbol{3 : 4 : 6}$
(factor 2)

4.   (a) $20 : 15 = \boldsymbol{4 : 3}$ (factor 5)

(b) $16 : 48 = \boldsymbol{1 : 3}$ (factor 16)

(c) $10 : 30 : 24 = \boldsymbol{5 : 15 : 12}$
(factor 2)

(d) $60 : 40 : 80 = \boldsymbol{3 : 2 : 4}$
(factor 20)

Exercise 9

1. (a) $\dfrac{5}{6}$ (b) $\dfrac{6}{11}$ (c) $\dfrac{6}{5}$

2. (a) $\dfrac{2}{3}$ (b) $\dfrac{3}{2}$

3. (a) $\dfrac{\text{number of children}}{\text{number of men and women}} = \dfrac{3}{6} = \dfrac{1}{2}$

    (b) $\dfrac{\text{number of men}}{\text{number of women}} = \dfrac{4}{2} = 2$

4. (a) $\dfrac{\text{Sumin's height}}{\text{Meihua's height}} = \dfrac{7}{5}$ (b) **7 : 5**

Exercise 10

1. 7 units = 42 cm
    1 unit = 42 ÷ 7 = 6 cm
    3 units = 6 × 3 = 18 cm
    The length of the shortest ribbon is **18 cm**.

2. 5 units = 75
    1 unit = 75 ÷ 5 = 15
    There are **15** more female teachers than male teachers.

Exercise 11

1. (a) Divide each unit for cars into
        three equal units. There will be 6
        units.
        6 : 3 : 5

    (b) number of motorcycles = 5 units
        number of cars = 6 units
        5 units = 25
        1 unit = 25 ÷ 5 = 5
        6 units = 5 × 6 = 30
        There are **30** cars.

2. (a) Divide each unit for David into
        two equal units. There will be 4
        units for David, and 3 for Henry.
        $\dfrac{\text{David's money}}{\text{Henry's money}} = \dfrac{4}{3}$

    (b) David has 1 more unit than
        Henry. Together they have 7
        equal units.
        1 unit = $60
        7 units = $60 × 7 = **$420**

Exercise 12

US›

1. (a)

Length (cm)	Width (cm)
5	3
25	15
50	30
75	45

(b)

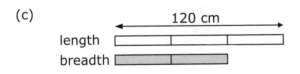

length
width

5 units = 120 cm
1 unit = 120 ÷ 5 = 24 cm
3 units = 24 × 3 = 72 cm
Width is **72 cm**.

(c)

length
width

5 units = 150 cm
1 unit = 150 ÷ 5 = 30 cm
3 units = 30 × 3 = 90 cm
Width is **90 cm**.

3d›

1. (a)

Length (cm)	Breadth (cm)
5	2
15	10
30	20
45	30

(b)

length
breadth

5 units = 120 cm
1 unit = 120 ÷ 3 = 40 cm
3 units = 40 × 2 = 80 cm
Breadth is **80 cm**.

(c)

length
breadth

5 units = 150 cm
1 unit = 150 ÷ 3 = 50 cm
3 units = 30 × 2 = 100 cm
Breadth is **100 cm**.

2.

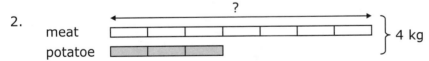

meat
potatoe

4 kg

total units = 7 + 3 = 10
4 kg = 4000 g
10 units = 4000 g
 1 unit = 4000 ÷ 10 = 400 g
 7 units = 400 × 7 = 2800 g = 2 kg 800 g
She used **2 kg 800 g** of meat.

(Or 2.8 kg or $2\frac{4}{5}$ kg)

3.

total units = 3 + 6 + 7 = 16
8 ℓ = 8000 ml
16 units = 8000 ml
  1 unit = 8000 ÷ 16 = 500 ml
  3 units = 500 × 3 = 1500 ml = 1 ℓ 500 ml
She used **1 ℓ 500 ml** of juice.

(Or 1.5 ℓ or $1\frac{1}{2}$ ℓ)

Exercise 13

1.   4 units = 32
      1 unit = 32 ÷ 4 = 8
      Meili's stickers = 8 × 3 = 24
      Suhua's stickers = 8 × 7 = 56
      One fourth of Suhua's stickers = 56 ÷ 4 = 14
      After giving them to Meili,
      Meili's stickers = 24 + 14 = 38
      Suhua's stickers = 56 − 14 = 42
      Meili's stickers : Suhua's stickers = 38 : 42 = **19 : 21**

2.   **US›** Joe's money : Conner's money = 2 : 4 = **1 : 2**
      3d› Ali's money : Hassan's money = 2 : 4 = **1 : 2**

Exercise 14

1.   5 units = 30
      1 unit = 30 ÷ 5 = 6
      Box A had 6 units. 6 units = 6 × 6 = 36
      Box A had **36** beads.

2.   3 units = $60
      1 unit = $60 ÷ 3 = $20
      John had 4 units at first. 4 units = $20 × 4 = $80
      John had **$80** at first.

3.   5 units = 100
      1 unit = 100 ÷ 5 = 20
      Susan has 2 units. 2 units = 20 × 2 = 40
      She had 50 tickets. Number of tickets she gave away = 50 − 40 = **10**

Review 1

1. Any multiple of 30.

2. (a) $(15 + 35) \div 5 \times 5$
   $= 50 \div 5 \times 5$
   $= 10 \times 5$
   $= \mathbf{50}$

   (b) $120 \div 12 + 7 \times 8$
   $= 10 + 7 \times 8$
   $= 10 + 56$
   $= \mathbf{66}$

3. (a) $2\frac{1}{4}$ $\frac{5}{4} = 1\frac{1}{4}$ $1\frac{11}{12}$ $\frac{12}{4} = 3$

   Order is $\mathbf{\frac{5}{4}}$, $\mathbf{1\frac{11}{12}}$, $\mathbf{2\frac{1}{4}}$, $\mathbf{\frac{12}{4}}$

   (b) $1\frac{2}{3} = 1\frac{16}{24}$ $\frac{45}{8} = 5\frac{5}{8}$ $1\frac{7}{8} = 1\frac{21}{24}$ $\frac{18}{6} = 3$

   Order is $\mathbf{1\frac{2}{3}}$, $\mathbf{1\frac{7}{8}}$, $\mathbf{\frac{18}{6}}$, $\mathbf{\frac{45}{8}}$

4. (a) $1\,\ell = 1000$ ml
   $\frac{3}{8}\,\ell = \frac{3}{8} \times 1000$ ml $= 375$
   $1\frac{3}{8}\,\ell = \mathbf{1375}$ ml

   (b) $\frac{3}{4}$ kg $= \frac{3}{4} \times 1000$ g $= 750$ g
   $4\frac{3}{4}$ kg $= \mathbf{4}$ kg $\mathbf{750}$ g

5. (a) **9** (x 3)   (b) **30** (x 5)   (c) **7** (÷ 3)   (d) **6** (÷ 4)

6. Total price $= \$4 \times 3 = \$12$
   Cost of third mug $=$ total price $-$ cost of other two mugs
   $= \$12 - \$p - \$3 = \mathbf{\$(9 - p)}$

7. (**US**› Heather's, **3d**› Meiling's) weight $= 38 + 6 = 44$ kg
   Average weight $= \dfrac{38 + 44}{2} = \dfrac{82}{2} = \mathbf{41\ kg}$
   Or: Average weight $=$ lower weight $+$ half of difference $= 38 + 3 = 41$ kg

8.
   boys
   girls

   12   ?

   1 unit = 12
   2 units = 12 × 2 = 24
   There are **24** more boys than girls.

9. Cost of pie $= \$1.20 \div 2 = \$0.60$
   Cost of 3 pies and 2 cakes $= (3 \times \$0.60) + (2 \times \$1.20) = \mathbf{\$4.20}$

10. $7.2\,\ell = 7200$ ml
    400 ml $\rightarrow 1$ min
    1 ml $\rightarrow \dfrac{1}{400}$ min
    7200 ml $\rightarrow \dfrac{1}{400} \times 7200$ min $= \dfrac{72}{4}$ min $= 18$ min
    It will take **18 min** for $7.2\,\ell$ to flow out of the tank.

11. Amount of honey used in 8 days = 0.27 kg × 8 = 2.16 kg
     Amount of honey left = 2.72 – 2.16 = **0.56 kg**

12. Fraction of girls = $1 - \dfrac{5}{8} = \dfrac{3}{8}$

     Number of girls = $\dfrac{3}{8} \times 720 = 3 \times 90 =$ **270**

13. Fraction of children that were girl scouts = $\dfrac{4}{5} \times \dfrac{2}{3} = \dfrac{\mathbf{8}}{\mathbf{15}}$

14.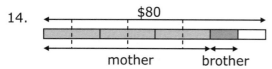

     8 units were given to her mother,   Or:
     leaving a remainder of 2 units, one of
     which was given to her brother.   Money left = $\dfrac{1}{2} \times \dfrac{1}{4} \times 80 = \dfrac{80}{8} = 10$
     8 units = $80
     1 unit = $80 ÷ 8 = $10
     She had **$10** left.

15. 2 units = $630
     1 unit = $630 ÷ 2 = $315
     3 units = $315 × 3 = $945
     He saves **$945**.

16. 9 units = 36
     1 unit = 36 ÷ 9 = 4
     2 units = 8
     The capacity of the smallest bucket is **8 ℓ.**

17. **US›** Russell's weight to Brooke's weight = **3 : 4**
     3d› Roslan's weight to Aminah's weight = **3 : 4**

18. (a) B is **3** times longer.
     (b) length of A : total length = **1 : 4**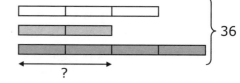

19. (a) $\dfrac{\text{number of boys}}{\text{number of girls}} = \dfrac{\mathbf{7}}{\mathbf{5}}$ (b) $\dfrac{\text{number of boys}}{\text{total}} = \dfrac{7}{7+5} = \dfrac{\mathbf{7}}{\mathbf{12}}$

20. (a) Number of adults : total = **3 : 4**   adults

                                                    children

     (b) $\dfrac{\text{number of children}}{\text{total}} = \dfrac{\mathbf{1}}{\mathbf{4}}$ (c) 1 unit = 207
                                                          4 units = 207 × 4 = 828
                                                          There are **828** people.

21.

students who wear glasses

$220 + 260 = 480$
3 units = 480
1 unit $= 480 \div 3 = 160$
5 units $= 160 \times 5 = 800$
There are **800** students.

Or: $\frac{3}{5}$ of the students = 480

$\frac{1}{5}$ of the students $= 480 \div 3 = 160$

All of the students $= 160 \times 5 = 800$

22. 4 units = 16 cm
1 unit $= 16 \div 4 = 4$ cm
3 units $= 4 \times 3 = 12$ cm = width
Perimeter $= 2 \times (16 + 12)$
$\qquad\qquad = 2 \times 28 =$ **56 cm**

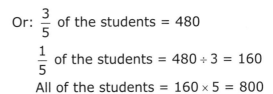

16 cm

23. Perimeter $= 2 \times$ (length) $\times$ (width)
$\qquad\qquad = 2 \times (7 \text{ units} + 4 \text{ units})$
$\qquad\qquad = 2 \times 11 \text{ units}$
$\qquad\qquad = 22 \text{ units}$
22 units = 44 cm
1 unit $= 44 \div 22 = 2$ cm
length = 7 units $= 7 \times 2$ cm = 14 cm
width = 4 units $= 4 \times 2$ cm = 8 cm
area $= 14$ cm $\times 8$ cm = **112 cm²**

24. length
width

length
width

$\xrightarrow{2}$

(a) 1 unit = 2 cm
5 units $= 5 \times 2 = 10$ cm
Original length was **10 cm**.

(b) final length $= 6 \times 2$ cm = 12 cm
width $= 3 \times 2$ cm = 6 cm
Area after the increase
$= 12$ cm $\times 6$ cm = **72 cm²**

25. Area A $= \frac{1}{2} \times 5 \times 3 = 7\frac{1}{2}$

Area B = Area C $= \frac{1}{2} \times 1 \times 4 = 2$

Area rectangle $= 5 \times 4 = 20$

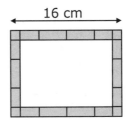

Shaded area = area of rectangle − area of 3 triangles $= 20 - 7\frac{1}{2} - 2 - 2 = \mathbf{8\frac{1}{2}}$ **cm²**

26. Height of top triangle $= 18 - 10 = 8$ cm
Area of top triangle $= \frac{1}{2} \times 10 \times 8 = 40$ cm²

Area of left triangle $= \frac{1}{2} \times 6 \times 10 = 30$ cm²

Area of square $= 10 \times 10 = 100$ cm²
Total area $= 100 + 40 + 30 =$ **170 cm²**

27. Find the cost of magazines in terms of the cost of comics.
2 magazines → 3 comics

$\quad$ 1 magazine → $\dfrac{3}{2}$ comics

$\quad$ 12 magazines → $\dfrac{3}{2}$ x 12 = 18 comics

$\quad$ 27 comics + 12 magazines cost $126 $\longrightarrow$ $\quad$ 27 comics + 18 comics cost $126
$\qquad\qquad\qquad\qquad\qquad\qquad\qquad\qquad\qquad$ 45 comics cost $126.
$\qquad\qquad\qquad\qquad\qquad\qquad\qquad\qquad\qquad$ 1 comic costs $126 ÷ 45 = **$2.80**

Or: If 3 comics cost the same as 2 magazines, find out how many comics he could have bought instead of the magazines. For 2 magazines, he could have bought 3 comics. So for 12 magazines, how many comic books could he buy? Set up a proportion:

$\dfrac{3 \text{ comics}}{2 \text{ magazines}} = \dfrac{? \text{ comics}}{12 \text{ magazines}}$. He could buy 18 comics for the same money as 12 magazines. If he just bought comics, he would have bought 27 + 18 = 45 comics.
45 comics cost $126
1 comic costs $126 ÷ 45 = $2.80

Or: Make equivalent units consisting of 3 comics and 2 magazines. 27 comics is 27 ÷ 3 = 9 units. 12 magazines = 12 ÷ 2 = 6 units.
9 units + 6 units = 15 units.
15 units cost $126
1 unit costs $126 ÷ 15 = $8.40
Since there are 3 comics in a unit then 3 comics cost $8.40
1 comic costs $8.40 ÷ 3 = $2.80

28.

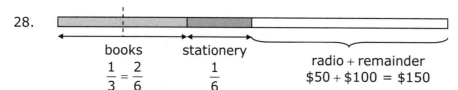

books $\qquad$ stationery $\qquad$ radio + remainder
$\dfrac{1}{3} = \dfrac{2}{6}$ $\qquad\quad$ $\dfrac{1}{6}$ $\qquad\qquad$ $50 + $100 = $150

He spent half his money on books and stationery $\left(\dfrac{2}{6} + \dfrac{1}{6} = \dfrac{3}{6} = \dfrac{1}{2}\right)$. So the amount for the radio and the amount left over is half his money.
All his money = 2 × $150 = **$300**

29.

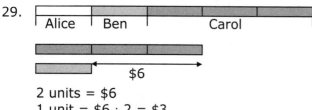

2 units = $6
1 unit = $6 ÷ 2 = $3
Ben received **$3**. 2 units = $6

30. Average weight = 3.2 kg = 3,200 g
    Total weight = 3,200 × 3 = 9,600 g
    If another 400 g is added, total
    weight would be 4 units.
    4 units = 9,600 g + 400 g = 10,000 g
    1 unit = 10,000 g ÷ 4 = 2,500 g
    Weight of C = 1 unit − 400 g = 2,500 g − 400 g = 2,100 g = **2 kg 100 g**

Exercise 15

1. (a) $\dfrac{25}{100} = \mathbf{25\%}$ (b) $\dfrac{20}{50} = \dfrac{40}{100} = \mathbf{40\%}$ (c) $\dfrac{84}{300} = \dfrac{28}{100} = \mathbf{28\%}$

2. (a) $\dfrac{3}{4} \times 100\% = \mathbf{75\%}$ (b) $\dfrac{1}{5} \times 100\% = \mathbf{20\%}$ (c) $\dfrac{7}{8} \times 100\% = \mathbf{87.5\%}$

3. (a) $\dfrac{48}{100} = \mathbf{48\%}$ (b) $\dfrac{6}{10} = \dfrac{60}{100} = \mathbf{60\%}$

   (c) $\dfrac{3}{5} \times 100\% = \mathbf{60\%}$ (d) $\dfrac{15}{75} \times 100\% = \mathbf{20\%}$

   (e) $\dfrac{6}{40} \times 100\% = \mathbf{15\%}$ (f) $\dfrac{5}{8} \times 100\% = \mathbf{62.5\%}$

   (g) $\dfrac{60}{80} \times 100\% = \mathbf{75\%}$ (h) $\dfrac{168}{700} \times 100\% = \mathbf{24\%}$

Exercise 16

1. (a) $2\% = \dfrac{2}{100} = \dfrac{\mathbf{1}}{\mathbf{50}}$ (b) $15\% = \dfrac{15}{100} = \dfrac{\mathbf{3}}{\mathbf{20}}$

   (c) $24\% = \dfrac{24}{100} = \dfrac{\mathbf{6}}{\mathbf{25}}$ (d) $45\% = \dfrac{45}{100} = \dfrac{\mathbf{9}}{\mathbf{20}}$

   (e) $60\% = \dfrac{60}{100} = \dfrac{\mathbf{3}}{\mathbf{5}}$ (f) $74\% = \dfrac{74}{100} = \dfrac{\mathbf{37}}{\mathbf{50}}$

2. (a) **30%**   (b) **8%**
   (c) **67%**   (d) **0.4%**
   (e) **2.5%**   (f) **38.5%**

3. (a) **0.02**   (b) **0.07**
   (c) **0.1**   (d) **0.8**
   (e) **0.25**   (f) **0.99**

Exercise 17

1. Total number on bus = $25 + 18 + 7 = 50$

   Percentage of people that are adults = $\dfrac{7}{50} \times 100 = \mathbf{14\%}$

2. Amount Samy receives = $180 - $45 - $63 = $72

   Percentage Samy receives = $\dfrac{72}{180} \times 100\% = \mathbf{40\%}$

3. Total money = $480 + $320 = $800

   Percentage spent on the television set = $\dfrac{480}{800} \times 100\% = \mathbf{60\%}$

4. Percentage that chose soccer = $100\% - 26\% - 12\% - 10\% = 52\%$

   Number of students that chose soccer = 52% of 400 = $\dfrac{52}{100} \times 400 = \mathbf{208}$

Exercise 18

1. (a)

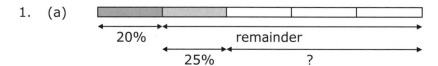

   Remainder = $100\% - 20\% = 80\%$
   Percentage of money left = 75% of the remainder
   75% of 80% = $\dfrac{75}{100} \times 80\% = \dfrac{3}{4} \times 80\% = 60\%$
   She had **60%** of her money left.
   Or: 20% is one fifth, there are four fifths in the remainder, 25% of those four fifths is one of the four fifths, and there are three fifths left, which is 60%.

   (b) 60% of $120 = $\dfrac{60}{100} \times $120 = \mathbf{\$72}$

2. Remainder = 45%
   80% of the remainder are children.

   80% of 45% = $\dfrac{80}{100} \times 45\% = 36\%$

   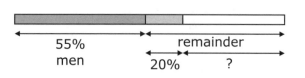

   36% of 1500 = $\dfrac{36}{100} \times 1500 = 540$

   There were **540** children.

Exercise 19

1. Increase = 10% of 5000 = 500
    5000 + 500 = 5500
    5500 people visited the fair the second week.

2. Discount = 25% of $400 = $\frac{1}{4}$ × $400 = $100

    Sale price = $400 − $100 = **$300**

3. Tax = 3% of $450 = $\frac{3}{100}$ × $450 = $13.50

    Cost of vase = $450 + $13.50 = **$463.50**

4. Increase in boys = 25% of 24 = $\frac{1}{4}$ × 24 = 6

    Decrease in girls = 10% of 20 = 2
    Overall change = +6 − 2 = +4, an **overall increase of 4**

Exercise 20

1. 2 m = 200 cm
    $\frac{80}{200}$ × 100% = **40%**

2. 1.5 kg = 1,500 g
    $\frac{750}{1500}$ × 100% = **50%**

3. 0.8 ℓ = 800 ml
    $\frac{120}{800}$ × 100% = **15%**

4. $\frac{15}{12}$ × 100% = **125%**

5. 1.2 km = 1,200 m
    $\frac{1200}{300}$ × 100% = **400%**

6. $\frac{2.5}{2}$ × 100% = **125%**

Exercise 21

1. (a) Discount = $25 − $19 = **$6**   (b) $\frac{6}{25}$ × 100% = **24%**

2. (a) Increase = $1500 − $1200 = **$300**   (b) $\frac{300}{1200}$ × 100% = **25%**

3. Increase = 36 − 24 = 12
    Percentage increase = $\frac{12}{24}$ × 100% = **50%**

4. Decrease = 1200 − 900 = 300
    Percentage decrease = $\frac{300}{1200}$ = **25%**

Exercise 22

1. Difference = 42 – 24 = 18

   Percent more boys than girls = $\dfrac{\text{difference}}{\text{\# girls}} \times 100\% = \dfrac{18}{24} \times 100\% = \textbf{75\%}$

2. Number of girls = 400 – 240 = 160
   Difference = 240 – 160 = 80

   Percent more boys than girls = $\dfrac{\text{difference}}{\text{\# girls}} \times 100\% = \dfrac{80}{160} \times 100\% = \textbf{50\%}$

US‹ 3. Difference = 15% of 6 gal = $\dfrac{15}{100} \times 6$ gal = 0.9 gal

   Cooking oil used this month = 6 gal – 0.9 gal = **5.1 gal**

3d‹ 3. Difference = 15% of 6 kg = $\dfrac{15}{100} \times 6$ kg = 0.9 kg

   Cooking oil used this month = 6 kg – 0.9 kg = **5.1 kg**

4. Difference = 14% of $600 = $\dfrac{14}{100} \times \$600 = \$84$

   Amount earned in Feb. = $600 + $84 = **$684**

Exercise 23

1. (a)

   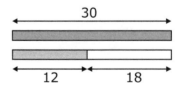

   clothes 60%   remainder
                      food 60%

   Amount spent on clothes = 60% of $50 = 6 × 10% of $50 = 6 × $5 = $30
   Amount left = $50 – $30 = $20
   Amount spent on food = 60% of $20 = 6 × 10% of $20 = 6 × $2 = $12
   Difference = $30 – $12 = **$18**

   (b) We want to find the percent more spent on clothes *than* on food. The base is the amount spent on food ($12). The amount being compared to the amount spent on food is the amount more spent on clothes ($18). We are finding the *difference* as a percentage of the food amount.

   30

   12   18

   $\dfrac{\text{difference}}{\text{food amount}} \times 100\% = \dfrac{18}{12} \times 100\% = \textbf{150\%}$

2.

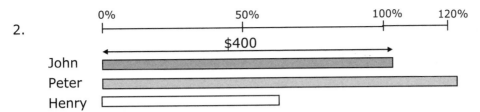

(a) John's money is 100%.

Peter's money = 120% of $400 = $\frac{120}{100} \times \$400 = \$480$

Henry's money = $480 ÷ 2 = $240
Amount they had in all = $400 + $480 + $240 = **$1120**

(b) $\frac{\text{Henry's money}}{\text{John's money}} = \frac{240}{400} \times 100\% = $ **60%**

Exercise 24

1. The total number of books is the base (100%).

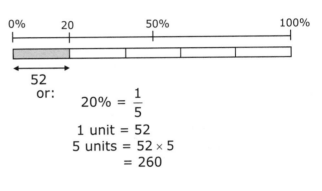

20% ⟶ 52

1% ⟶ $\frac{52}{20}$

100% ⟶ $\frac{52}{20} \times 100$

= 260

or:

20% = $\frac{1}{5}$

1 unit = 52
5 units = 52 × 5
= 260

He has **260** books altogether.

2. Meifen's money is the base.

75% of Meifen's money is $300.

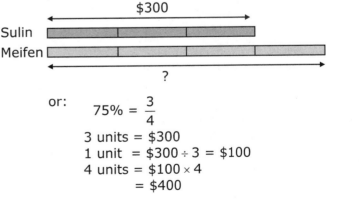

75% ⟶ $300

1% ⟶ $\$\frac{300}{75}$

100% ⟶ $\$\frac{300}{75} \times 100$

= $400

or:

75% = $\frac{3}{4}$

3 units = $300
1 unit = $300 ÷ 3 = $100
4 units = $100 × 4
= $400

Meifin saves **$400**.

3.   Peter's total money is 100%.
Percentage left = 40%
40% of the total money is $18.

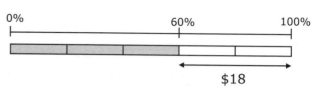

$18

$$40\% \longrightarrow \$18$$
$$1\% \longrightarrow \$\frac{18}{40}$$
$$100\% \longrightarrow \$\frac{18}{40} \times 100$$
$$= \$45$$

or:
$$40\% = \frac{4}{10} = \frac{2}{5}$$
2 units = $18
1 unit = $18 ÷ 2 = $9
5 units = $9 × 5
        = $45

He had **$45** at first.

4.   The total number of stamps is 100%.
Percentage left = 75%
75% of the total number of stamps is 450.

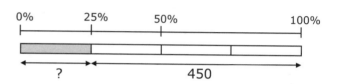

?   450

$$75\% \longrightarrow 450$$
$$1\% \longrightarrow \frac{450}{75}$$
$$25\% \longrightarrow \frac{450}{75} \times 25$$
$$= 150$$

or:
$$75\% = \frac{3}{4}$$
3 units = 450
1 unit = 450 ÷ 3 = 150

He gave away **150** stamps.

Exercise 25

1.   The usual price is the base (100%).
70% of the usual price is $42.

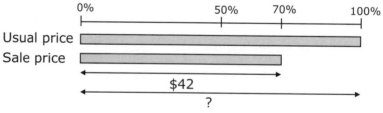

Usual price
Sale price

$42

?

$$70\% \longrightarrow \$42$$
$$1\% \longrightarrow \$\frac{42}{70}$$
$$100\% \longrightarrow \$\frac{42}{70} \times 100$$
$$= \$60$$

or:
$$70\% = \frac{7}{10}$$
7 units = $42
$$1 \text{ unit} = \$\frac{42}{7}$$
$$10 \text{ units} = \$\frac{42}{7} \times 10 = \$60$$

The usual price is **$60**.

2. The price before the increase is the base. 110% of the usual price is $2420.

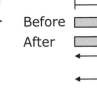

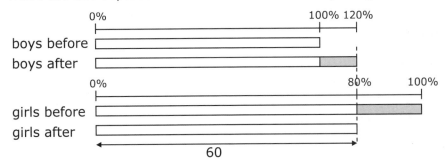

$110\% \longrightarrow \$2420$

$1\% \longrightarrow \$\dfrac{2420}{110}$

$100\% \longrightarrow \$\dfrac{2420}{110} \times 100 = \$2200$

The price before the increase was **$2200**.

3. There are two separate cases. The number of boys or girls before is the base.

120% of the original number of boys is 60.

$120\% \longrightarrow 60$

$1\% \longrightarrow \dfrac{60}{120}$

$100\% \longrightarrow \dfrac{60}{120} \times 100$

$= 50$

There were originally 50 boys.

80% of the original number of girls is 60.

$80\% \longrightarrow 60$

$1\% \longrightarrow \dfrac{60}{80}$

$100\% \longrightarrow \dfrac{60}{80} \times 100$

$= 75$

There were originally 75 girls.

Total membership before = 50 + 75 = 125
Total membership after = 60 + 60 = 120
There was an overall **decrease of 5 members**.

Exercise 26

1. 115% of the number of visitors on Saturday is 2300.

$115\% \longrightarrow 2300$

$1\% \longrightarrow \dfrac{2300}{115}$

$100\% \longrightarrow \dfrac{2300}{115} \times 100 = 2000$

There were **2000** visitors on Saturday.

2. She had 60% of 60% of her money left.

    60% of $60\% = \dfrac{60}{100} \times 60\%$

    $= 36\%$

    36% of her money is $90.

    $36\% \longrightarrow \$90$

    $1\% \longrightarrow \$\dfrac{90}{36}$

    $100\% \longrightarrow \$\dfrac{90}{36} \times 100$

    $= \$250$

    She had **$250** at first.

or: 60% of the remainder is 90.

    $60\% \longrightarrow 90$

    $1\% \longrightarrow \$\dfrac{90}{60}$

    $100\% \longrightarrow \$\dfrac{90}{60} \times 100 = \$150$

    60% of her money is $150.

    $60\% \longrightarrow \$150$

    $1\% \longrightarrow \$\dfrac{150}{60}$

    $100\% \longrightarrow \$\dfrac{150}{60} \times 100 = \$250$

3. The total number of stamps is the base (100%).
    There are 100% – 30% = 70% U.S. stamps.
    The difference in the number of (**US›** U.S. and Canadian, **3d›** Singapore and Malaysian stamps) is 70% – 30% = 40% of the total stamps.
    The difference is 500.
    So 40% of the total stamps is 500 stamps.

    $40\% \longrightarrow 500$

    $1\% \longrightarrow \dfrac{500}{40}$

    $100\% \longrightarrow \dfrac{500}{40} \times 100 = 1250$

    He has **1250** stamps altogether.

4. 25% of the boys in the club is 36.

    $25\% \longrightarrow 36$

    $1\% \longrightarrow \dfrac{36}{25}$

    $100\% \longrightarrow \dfrac{36}{25} \times 100 = 144$

    There are **144** boys.

Review 2

1. Add 3 0's. **4,995,000**

2. **3.59 kg** (The others are all 3, correct to the nearest kg.)

3. 24: 1, 2, 3, 4, 6, 8, 12, 24
    32: 1, 2, 4, 8, 16, 32
    Common factors: 1, **2, 4, 8**

4. (a) **7** h **40** min (b) **3** h **40** min

5. (a) **100** (b) **10**

6. **3.09**

7. (a) $\dfrac{16}{200} = \dfrac{8}{100} = \mathbf{8\%}$ (b) $0.046 \times 100\% = \mathbf{4.6\%}$

8. Number of girls $= \dfrac{7}{8} \times 40 = 35$

    Number of girls that walk to school $= \dfrac{3}{5} \times 35 = \mathbf{21}$

9. Amount divided into two parts $= 1 - \dfrac{1}{4} = \dfrac{3}{4}$

    Fraction each part is of whole cake $= \dfrac{1}{2} \times \dfrac{3}{4} = \dfrac{\mathbf{3}}{\mathbf{8}}$

10. **1 : 4**

11.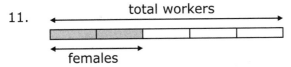

    number of male workers : number of female workers = **3 : 2**

12. US› 3d›
    Joe Ali
    Colin Gopal

    36 kg

    (a) $\dfrac{\text{Joe's weight}}{\text{Colin's weight}} = \dfrac{2}{3}$ (a) $\dfrac{\text{Ali's weight}}{\text{Gopal's weight}} = \dfrac{2}{3}$

    (b) 3 units = 36 kg

    1 unit $= \dfrac{36}{3}$ kg = 12 kg

    (**US›** Joe's, **3d›** Ali's) weight $= 2 \times 12$ kg = 24 kg
    If (**US›** Joe, **3d›** Ali) gains 3 kg, his new weight becomes $24 + 3 = 27$ kg
    New ratio = 27 : 36 = **3 : 4** (divide both by 9)

13. (a) 400 : 600 = **2 : 3** (divide both by 200)
    (b) 5 units = 500 g
    1 unit = 500 ÷ 5 = 100 g
    2 units = 100 × 2 = 200 g
    She needs **200 g** of cashews.

    cashews
    peanuts
    } 500 g

14. $\dfrac{2}{8} = \dfrac{1}{4} = \mathbf{25\%}$

15.   Discount = 20% of $75 = $\dfrac{20}{100} \times \$75 = \$15$

     Sale price = $75 – $15 = **$60**

16.   Interest = 4% of $840 = $\dfrac{4}{100} \times \$840 =$ **$33.60**

17.   Increase = 50 – 40 = 10

     Percent increase = $\dfrac{10}{40} \times 100\% =$ **25%**

18.   20% of $1200 = $\dfrac{1}{5} \times \$1200 = \$240$

     20% of $1500 = $\dfrac{1}{5} \times \$1500 = \$300$ or: $1500 – $1200 = $300

     Increased savings = $300 – $240 = $60   20% of $300 = $\dfrac{1}{5} \times \$300 = \$60$

     He can save **$60** more each month.

19.

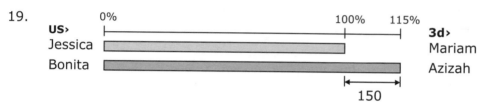

     Total stamps = 215% of (**US›** Jessica's, **3d›** Mariam's) stamps

     15% of (**US›** Jessica's, **3d›** Mariam's) stamps is 150.

      15% $\longrightarrow$ 150

     215% $\longrightarrow \dfrac{150}{15} \times 215 = 2{,}150$

     They have **2150** stamps altogether.

20.   Percentage of marbles that are green = 100% – 40% – 20% = 40%

     40% of the marbles is 80.

      40% $\longrightarrow$ 80

     100% $\longrightarrow \dfrac{80}{40} \times 100 = 200$

     There are **200** marbles.

21.

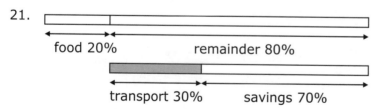

     Percentage of salary saved = 70% of 80% = $\dfrac{7}{10} \times 80\% =$ **56%**

22. (a) 8 h $\longrightarrow$ \$20

     1 h $\longrightarrow$ \$$\dfrac{20}{8}$ = **\$2.50**

   (b) 10 h $\longrightarrow$ \$2.50 × 10 = **\$25**

   (c) \$25 $\longrightarrow$ 10
        \$50 $\longrightarrow$ 10 × 2 = **20 h**

23. 25 revolutions $\longrightarrow$ 5 min

     1 revolution $\longrightarrow$ $\dfrac{5}{25}$ = $\dfrac{1}{5}$ min

     30 revolutions $\longrightarrow$ $\dfrac{1}{5}$ × 30 = 6 min

   It will take **6 minutes** to make 30 revolutions.

24. Length = 2 × (12 cm + 8 cm) = 2 × 20 cm = **40 cm**

25. Area of shaded region = area of square – area of triangle

   $$= (12 × 12) - (\dfrac{1}{2} × 12 × 4) = 144 - 24 = \textbf{120 cm}^2$$

26. Answers may vary.

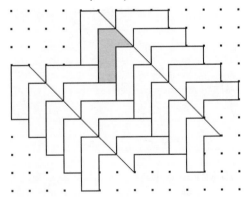

Exercise 27

1. (a) Speed = $\dfrac{\text{Distance}}{\text{Time}}$ = $\dfrac{150}{3}$ = **50 km/h**

   (b) Speed = $\dfrac{\text{Distance}}{\text{Time}}$ = $\dfrac{450}{6}$ = **75 km/h**

   (c) 1 h $\longrightarrow$ 45 km   or: Distance = Speed × Time
        2 h $\longrightarrow$ 45 × 2 = **90 km**   = 45 km/h × 2 h = 90 km

(d)   60 km $\longrightarrow$ 1 h

   330 km $\longrightarrow \dfrac{1}{60} \times 330$ or: Time $= \dfrac{\text{Distance}}{\text{Speed}}$

$\qquad\qquad\qquad = \mathbf{5\dfrac{1}{2}\ h}$ $= \dfrac{330\ \text{km}}{60\ \text{km/h}} = 5\dfrac{1}{2}\ h$

Exercise 28

1. Speed $= \dfrac{\text{Distance}}{\text{Time}} = \dfrac{216\ \text{km}}{4\ \text{h}} = \mathbf{54\ km/h}$

2. Speed $= \dfrac{\text{Distance}}{\text{Time}} = \dfrac{800\ \text{m}}{20\ \text{min}} = \mathbf{40\ m/min}$

3. Distance $=$ Speed $\times$ Time   or: 1 h $\longrightarrow$ 80 km
    $= 80$ km/h $\times 5$ h   5 h $\longrightarrow 80 \times 5$
    $= \mathbf{400\ km}$ $= 400$ km

4. Distance $=$ Speed $\times$ Time   or: 1 min $\longrightarrow$ 60 m
    $= 60$ m/min $\times 15$ min   15 min $\longrightarrow 60 \times 15$
    $= \mathbf{900\ m}$ $= 900$ m

US›

5. Time $= \dfrac{\text{Distance}}{\text{Speed}}$ or: 60 mi $\longrightarrow$ 1 h

    $= \dfrac{30\ \text{mi}}{60\ \text{mi/h}}$ 30 mi $\longrightarrow \dfrac{1}{60} \times 30$

    $= \mathbf{\dfrac{1}{2}\ h}$ $= \dfrac{1}{2}\ h$

3d›

5. Time $= \dfrac{\text{Distance}}{\text{Speed}}$ or: 60 km $\longrightarrow$ 1 h

    $= \dfrac{30\ \text{km}}{60\ \text{km/h}}$ 30 km $\longrightarrow \dfrac{1}{60} \times 30$

    $= \mathbf{\dfrac{1}{2}\ h}$ $= \dfrac{1}{2}\ h$

6. Time $= \dfrac{\text{Distance}}{\text{Speed}}$ or: 80 km $\longrightarrow$ 1 h

    $= \dfrac{240\ \text{km}}{80\ \text{km/h}}$ 240 km $\longrightarrow \dfrac{1}{80} \times 240$

    $= \mathbf{3\ h}$ $= 3$ h

Exercise 29

1. (a)   Speed = $\dfrac{\text{Distance}}{\text{Time}} = \dfrac{800 \text{ m}}{2 \text{ min}}$ = **400 m/min**

    (b)   Distance = Speed × Time   or: 1 min ⟶ 400 m
               = 400 m/min × 5 min   5 min ⟶ 400 × 5
               = 2,000 m   = 2,000 m
               = **2 km**

2. (a)   Speed = $\dfrac{\text{Distance}}{\text{Time}} = \dfrac{150 \text{ km}}{2 \text{ h}}$ = **75 km/h**

    (b)   Time = $\dfrac{\text{Distance}}{\text{Speed}}$ or: 60 km ⟶ 1 h

               = $\dfrac{150 \text{ km}}{60 \text{ km/h}}$ 150 km ⟶ $\dfrac{1}{60}$ × 150

               = **$2\dfrac{1}{2}$ h**   = $2\dfrac{1}{2}$ h

3. Time = $\dfrac{\text{Distance}}{\text{Speed}}$ or: 70 m ⟶ 1 min

         = $\dfrac{910 \text{ m}}{70 \text{ m/min}}$ 910 m ⟶ $\dfrac{1}{70}$ × 910

         = 13 min   = 13 min
    7:30 a.m. + 13 min = 7:43 a.m.
    He arrived at **7:43 a.m.**

4.

   $\overset{\text{80 m/min, 6 min}}{\longmapsto\!\!\longrightarrow}$

   $\overset{\text{60 m/min, ? min}}{\longmapsto\!\longrightarrow}$

   The distance in both cases is the same.
   Distance = Speed × Time
              = 80 m/min × 6 min
              = 480 m
   New Time = $\dfrac{\text{Distance}}{\text{Speed}} = \dfrac{480 \text{ m}}{60 \text{ m/min}}$ = 8 min
   It would take her **8 min** at the new speed.

Exercise 30

1. Total distance is the distance for each part of the trip.

    Distance = (6 km/h × $\dfrac{1}{2}$ h) + (8 km/h × $\dfrac{1}{4}$ h) = 3 km + 2 km = **5 km**

2.

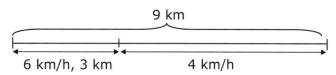

9 km

6 km/h, 3 km   4 km/h

Total time = time for both parts
To find the time for the second part, the distance is needed.
Distance for second part = 9 km − 3 km = 6 km

Total time = $\dfrac{3 \text{ km}}{6 \text{ km/h}}$ + $\dfrac{6 \text{ km}}{4 \text{ km/h}}$ = $\dfrac{1}{2}$ h + $\dfrac{3}{2}$ h = **2 h**

US›

3.   To find David's average speed, we need to find the distance he traveled.
We can find the distance Ryan traveled from Town X to Town Y.
Distance = 4 h × 10 km/h = 40 km
During the 4 hours, David traveled 2 km less.
Distance David traveled = 40 − 2 = 38 km

David's average speed = $\dfrac{38 \text{ km}}{4 \text{ h}}$ = **9$\dfrac{1}{2}$ km/h**

3d›

3.   To find Gopal's average speed, we need to find the distance he traveled.
We can find the distance Raju traveled from Town X to Town Y.
Distance = 4 h × 10 km/h = 40 km
During the 4 hours, Gopal traveled 2 km less.
Distance Gopal traveled = 40 − 2 = 38 km

Gopal's average speed = $\dfrac{38 \text{ km}}{4 \text{ h}}$ = **9$\dfrac{1}{2}$ km/h**

4.   (a)   Total time = $\dfrac{44 \text{ km}}{88 \text{ km/h}}$ + $\dfrac{96 \text{ km}}{64 \text{ km/h}}$ = $\dfrac{1}{2}$ h + $\dfrac{3}{2}$ h = **2 h**

(b)   Average speed = $\dfrac{44 \text{ km} + 96 \text{ km}}{2 \text{ h}}$ = $\dfrac{140}{2}$ km/h = **70 km/h**

5.   (a)   Total distance = (70 km/h × 1 h) + (64 km/h × 2 h)
= 70 km + 128 km
= **198 km**

(b)   Average speed = $\dfrac{198 \text{ km}}{1 \text{ h} + 2 \text{ h}}$ = $\dfrac{198}{3}$ km/h = **66 km/h**

Exercise 31

1. To find the average speed, we need to find the total distance and time. To do so, we need to find the distance and time for each part.

    We can find the distance for the last $\frac{2}{5}$ of the trip.

    Distance for 2nd part = 60 km/h $\times$ 1 h = 60 km

    $\frac{2}{5}$ of the trip = 60 km

    $\frac{1}{5}$ of the trip = $\frac{60}{2}$ = 30 km

    $\frac{5}{5}$ of the trip = 30 $\times$ 5 = 150 km

    Total time = 2 h + 1 h = 3 h

    Average speed = $\frac{150 \text{ km}}{3 \text{ h}}$ = **50 km/h**

2. We know the time for both parts of the trip and the distance for one part. We need to find the distance for the other part.

    Fraction of the trip covered in the 2nd part = $1 - \frac{8}{15}$ = $\frac{7}{15}$

    $\frac{7}{15}$ of the trip = 14 km

    $\frac{15}{15}$ of the trip = $\frac{14}{7} \times 15$ = 30 km

    Total time = 2 h + 2 h = 4 h

    Average speed = $\frac{30 \text{ km}}{4 \text{ h}}$ = **7.5 km/h**

Review 3

1. **0.001**

2. **21** and **28**

3. **69.51**

4. (a) **1000**

    (b) $8 \times \frac{2}{3} = \frac{2}{3} + \frac{2}{3} + \left(\frac{2}{3} + \frac{2}{3} + \frac{2}{3} + \frac{2}{3} + \frac{2}{3} + \frac{2}{3} \right)$

    $8 \times \frac{2}{3} = \frac{2}{3} + \frac{2}{3} + \left(\mathbf{6} \times \frac{2}{3} \right)$

5. $\frac{1}{4} + \frac{2}{5} = \frac{5}{20} + \frac{8}{20} = \frac{13}{20} = \frac{65}{100}$ = **65%**

6. $800 \times 30¢ = 24,000¢ =$ **\$240.00**

7. $\$2.50 \longrightarrow 5$ pens

　　$\$1 \longrightarrow \dfrac{5}{2.50}$ pens

　　$\$20 \longrightarrow \dfrac{5}{2.50} \times 20 = \dfrac{50}{25} \times 20 =$ **40** pens

8. $3 - 1\dfrac{2}{5} = 2 - \dfrac{2}{5} = 1\dfrac{3}{5}$ **$1\dfrac{3}{5}$** ℓ is needed.

9. $1\ \ell\ 200$ ml $= 1,200$ ml
    $400 : 1,200 =$ **1 : 3**

10. 5 units $= 2\ \ell$

　　2 units $= \dfrac{2}{5} \times 2 = \dfrac{4}{5}$ **$\ell =$ 0.80 ℓ**

$\left.\begin{array}{}\end{array}\right\} 2\ \ell$

11. $\dfrac{1}{2}$ h $= 30$ min

　　30 min $\longrightarrow 60$ soldiers

　　10 min $\longrightarrow \dfrac{60}{3} =$ **20** soldiers

12. Time $= \dfrac{\text{Distance}}{\text{Speed}}$

　　$= \dfrac{4\ \text{km}}{16\ \text{km/h}}$

　　$= \dfrac{1}{4}$ h $=$ **15 min**

　　or: 16 km $\longrightarrow 1$ h

　　　　1 km $\longrightarrow \dfrac{1}{16}$ h

　　　　4 km $\longrightarrow \dfrac{1}{16} \times 4$ h

　　　　　　$= \dfrac{1}{4}$ h $= 15$ min

US›

13. Alyssa's savings $= \$46$
    Renee's savings $= 3 \times$ Alyssa's savings $= 3 \times \$46 = \$138$
    Betty's savings $=$ Renee's savings $- \$40 = \$138 - \$40 = \$98$
    Average savings $= \dfrac{46 + 138 + 98}{3} = \dfrac{282}{3} =$ **\$94**

3d›

13. Ailian's savings $= \$46$
    Rani's savings $= 3 \times$ Ailian's savings $= 3 \times \$46 = \$138$
    Betty's savings $=$ Rani's savings $- \$40 = \$138 - \$40 = \$98$
    Average savings $= \dfrac{46 + 138 + 98}{3} = \dfrac{282}{3} =$ **\$94**

14. 1 unit = 15 cm
7 units = 15 × 7 = 105 cm
Jane's height is **105 cm**.

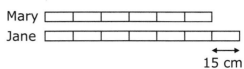

15.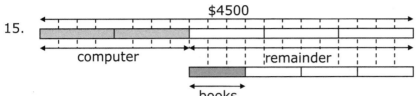

Divide total into 20 units.
20 units = $4500

$1 \text{ unit} = \$\dfrac{4500}{20}$

$3 \text{ units} = \$\dfrac{4500}{20} \times 3 = \$675$

He spent **$675** on books.

or: $\dfrac{1}{4}$ of the remainder $= \dfrac{1}{4} \times \dfrac{3}{5} = \dfrac{3}{20}$

$\dfrac{3}{20}$ of $4500 $= \dfrac{3}{20} \times \$4500 = \$675$

or: $\dfrac{3}{5} \times \$4500 = \$2,700$

$\dfrac{1}{4} \times \$2700 = \$675$

16.

men   women children

Divide the total into 8 units.
Men = 5 units
Women = 2 units
Children = 1 unit
$\dfrac{1}{8} \times 100\% = 12.5\%$

12.5% of the participants are children.

or: Fraction of participants that are

children $= 1 - \dfrac{5}{8} - \dfrac{1}{4} = \dfrac{8}{8} - \dfrac{5}{8} - \dfrac{2}{8} = \dfrac{1}{8}$

Percentage $= \dfrac{1}{8} \times 100\% = 12.5\%$

17. Discount = $2800 – $2380 = 420

Percent discount $= \dfrac{420}{2800} \times 100\% = \mathbf{15\%}$

18. A |—————→ 3 h, 80 km/h | B
         | 60 km/h ←—————
                                            1:00 pm

Distance = 80 km/h × 3 h = 240 km

Time for return $= \dfrac{240 \text{ km}}{60 \text{ km/h}} = 4 \text{ h}$

4 h after 1:00 p.m. is 5:00 p.m.
He arrived back at Town A at **5:00 p.m.**

19. Total cost of the 5 books = $21
     Total cost of 2 of the books = $7.80 × 2 = $15.60
     Cost of remaining 3 books = $21 − $15.60 = $5.40

     Average cost of remaining 3 books = $$\dfrac{5.40}{3}$ = **\$1.80**

20. Total pages read in 6 days = 40 × 6 = 240 pages

     $\dfrac{2}{3}$ of the book = 240 pages

     $\dfrac{3}{3}$ of the book = $\dfrac{240}{2}$ × 3 = 360

     She read 360 pages in 8 days.

     Average pages read per day = $\dfrac{360}{8}$ = **45**

21. (a) Number of families with 2 or more children = 40 + 14 + 5 = **60**

     (b) Number of families with less than 2 children = 30 + 10 = 40
          Ratio = 60 : 40 = **3 : 2**

22. Amount spent = (6 × $2.50) + (7 × $0.80) = $15 + $5.60 = $20.60

     She had $\dfrac{3}{5}$ of her money left.

     $\dfrac{2}{5}$ of her money = $20.60

     $\dfrac{1}{5}$ of her money = $$\dfrac{20.60}{2}$

     $\dfrac{3}{5}$ of her money = $$\dfrac{20.60}{2}$ × 3 = **\$30.90**

23. The number of girls stays the same.

     boys : girls
     Before   3 : 2   = 9 : 6
     After   2 : 3   = 4 : 6

     Number of units of boys that leave
     = 9 − 4 = 5
     5 units = 30

     1 unit = $\dfrac{30}{5}$

     9 units = $\dfrac{30}{5}$ × 9 = 54

     There were **54** boys at first.

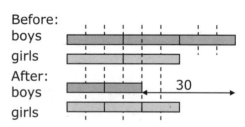

Before:
boys
girls
After:
boys
girls
30

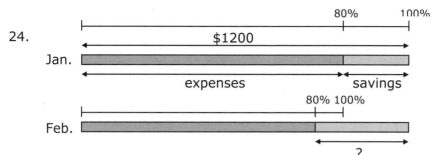

24.

Expenses in Jan. = 80% of \$1,200 = $\dfrac{80}{100}$ × \$1,200 = \$960

Expenses in Feb. = 90% of \$960 = $\dfrac{90}{100}$ × \$960 = \$864

Savings in Feb. = \$1,200 − \$864 = **\$336**

25.
8:30 a.m.   1:30 p.m.

P   ⟶   Peter 60 km/h   Q

9:30 a.m.   John ? km/h   1:30 p.m.

Peter's time = 5 h
John's time = 4 h
Distance = Peter's speed × Peter's time = 60 km/h × 5 h = 300 km

John's speed = $\dfrac{300\ km}{4\ h}$ = **75 km/h**

Revision 4

1. $\dfrac{1}{4} + \dfrac{1}{8} = \dfrac{\mathbf{3}}{\mathbf{8}}$

2. (a) **12**   (b) $\dfrac{\mathbf{3}}{\mathbf{8}}$ (c) $\dfrac{\mathbf{3}}{\mathbf{5}}$ (d) **25**

3. $\dfrac{\mathbf{6}}{\mathbf{8}}$

4. (a) **0.43**   (b) **2.44**

5. (a) $1\dfrac{3}{4} + 2\dfrac{7}{8} = 3\dfrac{6}{8} + \dfrac{7}{8} = 3\dfrac{5}{8} + \dfrac{8}{8} = \mathbf{4\dfrac{5}{8}}$

   (b) $4\dfrac{5}{12} - 2\dfrac{3}{4} = 2\dfrac{5}{12} - \dfrac{9}{12} = 2 - \dfrac{9}{12} + \dfrac{5}{12} = 1\dfrac{3}{12} + \dfrac{5}{12} = 1\dfrac{8}{12} = \mathbf{1\dfrac{2}{3}}$

   (c) $\dfrac{5}{8} \times 4 = \dfrac{5 \times 4}{8} = \dfrac{5}{2} = \mathbf{2\dfrac{1}{2}}$ (d) $\dfrac{3}{10} \times \dfrac{5}{12} = \dfrac{\cancel{3}^{1} \times \cancel{5}^{1}}{\cancel{10}_{2} \times \cancel{12}_{4}} = \dfrac{\mathbf{1}}{\mathbf{8}}$

   (e) $\dfrac{3}{8} \div 6 = \dfrac{\cancel{3}^{1}}{8} \times \dfrac{1}{\cancel{6}_{2}} = \dfrac{\mathbf{1}}{\mathbf{16}}$ (f) $\dfrac{5}{9} \div 5 = \dfrac{\cancel{5}^{1}}{9} \times \dfrac{1}{\cancel{5}_{1}} = \dfrac{\mathbf{1}}{\mathbf{9}}$

6. $\dfrac{3}{4} = 75\%$ $0.81 = 81\%$ $\dfrac{11}{8}$ is greater than 100%.

     65% is the smallest.

7. $\dfrac{2}{3}$ of a number = 0.3

     $\dfrac{1}{3}$ of a number = $\dfrac{0.3}{2}$

     $\dfrac{3}{3}$ of a number = $\dfrac{0.3}{2} \times 3 = \textbf{0.45}$

8. $36\% = \dfrac{36}{100} = \dfrac{\textbf{9}}{\textbf{25}}$

9.   45% of 6 km = $\dfrac{45}{100} \times 6$ km = **2.7 km**

10.   The remainder is $1 - \dfrac{3}{5} = \dfrac{2}{5}$

     Fraction given to son = $\dfrac{1}{4}$ of $\dfrac{2}{5} = \dfrac{1}{4} \times \dfrac{2}{5} = \dfrac{\textbf{1}}{\textbf{10}}$

11.   The bicycle cost $\dfrac{2}{9}$ less than its usual price.

     It cost $28 less than its usual price.

     $\dfrac{2}{9}$ of its usual price = $28

     $\dfrac{7}{9}$ of its usual price = $\$\dfrac{28}{2} \times 7 = \$98$

     He paid **$98**.

12.   The remainder is **$850** – $400 = $450

     She saved 60% of the remainder.

     60% of $450 = $\dfrac{60}{100} \times \$450 = \$270$

     She saved **$270**.

13.   Percent buses = 100% – 60% – 15% = 25%

     25% of the vehicles is 10.

     25% → 10

     60% → $\dfrac{10}{25} \times 60 = 24$

     There are **24** trucks.

14. Fraction of the people that are men $= \dfrac{2}{5} = \dfrac{16}{40}$

Fraction of the people that are women $= \dfrac{3}{8} = \dfrac{15}{40}$

Fraction of the people that are children $= \dfrac{40}{40} - \dfrac{16}{40} - \dfrac{15}{40} = \dfrac{9}{40}$

Ratio $= \dfrac{16}{40} : \dfrac{15}{40} : \dfrac{9}{40} = \mathbf{16 : 15 : 9}$

US›

15.
```
        Adam : Peter
Before   5  :  6  = 5 : 6
After    1  :  2  = 3 : 6
```

Adam gives away 2 units, or 40

2 units = 40

$5 \text{ units} = \dfrac{40}{2} \times 5 = 100$

Adam had **100** stamps at first.

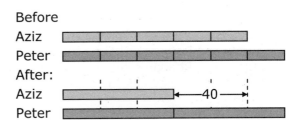

Before
Adam
Peter
After:
Adam
Peter
40

3d›

15.
```
        Aziz : Peter
Before   5  :  6  = 5 : 6
After    1  :  2  = 3 : 6
```

Aziz gives away 2 units, or 40

2 units = 40

$5 \text{ units} = \dfrac{40}{2} \times 5 = 100$

Aziz had **100** stamps at first.

Before
Aziz
Peter
After:
Aziz
Peter
40

16. $20 \text{ min} = \dfrac{1}{3} \text{ h}$

Distance $= 12 \text{ km/h} \times \dfrac{1}{3} \text{ h} = \mathbf{4 \text{ km}}$

17. Area = area of top triangle + area of rectangle + area of right triangle

$= (\dfrac{1}{2} \times 15 \times 5) + (15 \times 5) + (\dfrac{1}{2} \times 12 \times 5)$

$= 37\dfrac{1}{2} + 75 + 30$

$= \mathbf{142.5 \text{ cm}^2}$

18. (a) 13   (b) Thursday

(c) Average $= \dfrac{10 + 6 + 13 + 16 + 14}{5} = \dfrac{59}{5} = 11\dfrac{4}{5} = \mathbf{11.8}$

19. Area $= 2 \times (9 \times 9) + 4 \times (4 \times 9) = 162 + 144 = \mathbf{306 \text{ cm}^2}$

20. (a) no   (b) yes   (c) yes   (d) no

22.

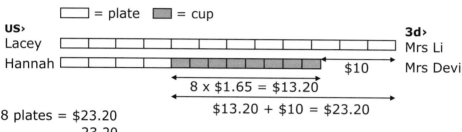

8 plates = $23.20

1 plate = $$\dfrac{23.20}{8} = \textbf{\$2.90}$$

22. Amount David and Ben received
   = 2 × $36 = $72
   Amount Ben received
   = $\dfrac{1}{3}$ × $72 = **$24**

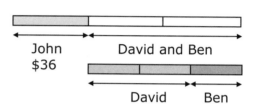

24. Laura's share = $16
   Reagan's share = $4 more than Laura's share = $4 + $16 = $20
   Bridget's share was 40%.
   Laura's and Reagan's share was 100% – 40% = 60%
   Laura's and Reagan's share was $16 + $20 = $36
   60% of the money is $36.
      60% → $36
      1% → $$\dfrac{36}{60}$$
   100% → $$\dfrac{36}{60} \times 100 = \$60$$
   They shared **$60**.

25.

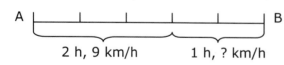

   Distance for first $\dfrac{3}{5}$ of the journey = 9 km/h × 2 h = 18 km

   Distance for $\dfrac{1}{5}$ of the journey = $\dfrac{18}{5}$ km

   Distance for last $\dfrac{2}{5}$ of the journey = $\dfrac{18}{3} \times 2 = 12$ km

   Average speed for last part = $\dfrac{12 \text{ km}}{1 \text{ h}}$ = **12 km/h**

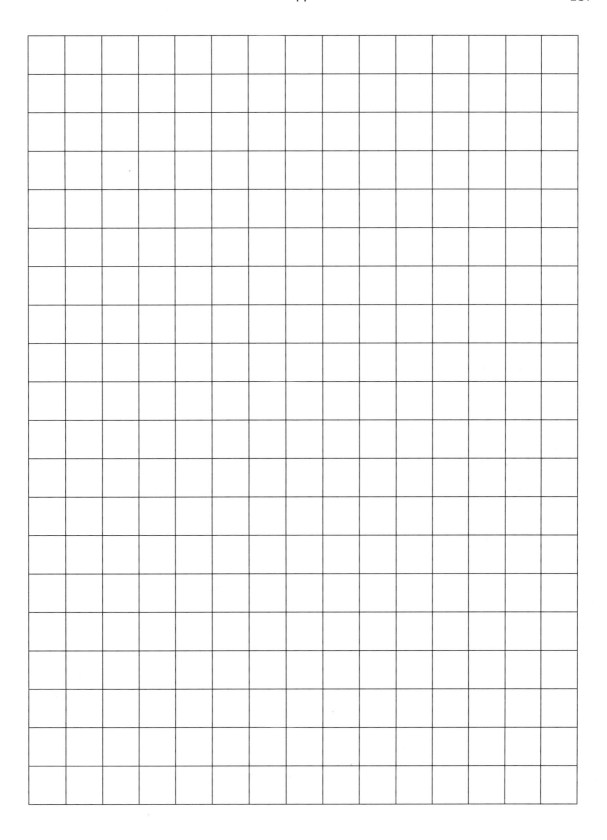